Stockings
without
Suspenders

Stockings without Suspenders

by
Irene Southern

Pharaoh
Press

Stockings without Suspenders
ISBN 1 9 01442 004

First Published in 1996 by Pharaoh Press, Liverpool

Cover illustration: Angelo Rinaldi, Artists Partners

Typeset by

Liverpool, L3 4BD

Printed and bound by WBC Book Manufacturers, Mid Glam.

Dedicated To

Mike, my partner
Gaynor and Terry
Wayne and Lois
Wayne and Philip
Phyllis and Tommy
Jack
Angela

1

What a start to the year. It was 1992 and January brought the bad weather. It was freezing outside and it had been doing its best to snow all day, not that the snow would stick as it had been raining as well.

It wasn't just the weather that had made me feel cold, but the big brown envelope I had in my hand. On the top was a red stamp that read 'confidential'. I had asked for its contents just before Christmas, so I knew what to expect. I wanted the truth and here it was – my Mum's Coroner's Report, forty-four years late. Well, I had to start somewhere to find my identity. Just who was I?

It had started three years ago. All my life I thought my Dad was dead. Had he died in the war or what? No-one would say, but three years ago I had news that my Dad was in Hobart, a town in Tasmania, Australia. I was up Breck Road doing some shopping, when who was standing at the counter waiting to be served but an old neighbour I hadn't seen for years.

"Hello, Mrs Williams, how are you?"

Mrs Williams turned round and tried to put a name to my face.

"Mrs Williams, it's Joyce Miller."

"My God! How are you, love? How's the family? Tell you the truth, I'd have walked past you. Haven't you changed!"

"We all change over the years, Mrs Williams, for the best I hope."

"How is your Jeanette and Gordon?"

"Oh, they're both married now, with families."

"My God! Doesn't time fly? I remember you three as babies, playing in the street — and here you are now with babies of your own. Your Mum would have been proud the way you all turned out. I saw Jeanette a few years ago, she's the spit of your Mum."

"Yes, I think I took after my Dad. Do you remember what he looked like?"

"Oh, Joyce, it was years ago! I know he used to go away to sea, so we only saw him now and again. You know what it was like in them days, just after the war an' all. The last we heard he jumped ship back in Australia. Must have gone back home."

"Home? What do you mean?"

"He came from Australia. Didn't you know?"

"No, I didn't."

"Yeah, your Nan used to tell me about him."

"What part?"

"Now, if I remember right it was, er, let me think, oh yeah, Tasmania – Hobart that's it. Aye, love, I'm sorry I thought you knew. Didn't your Nan ever tell you?"

"No, Nan never talked about him. I wish she had. So he could be alive?"

"Could be, but don't forget love, he would be getting on now, could even be dead."

Mrs Williams walked away after telling me to look after myself. I stood there waiting to be served with so many thoughts going through my mind.

After all these years was it true, my Dad was not dead?

Why had Nan said he was when we had asked? Jeanette, Gordon and myself had asked her over the years to tell us about him, and she always said the same: "He died just after Joyce was born, he had consumption and was taken to Broadgreen Hospital and died in there."

We never thought to ask where he was buried. As

children you never knew what happened to dead people, they died and that was that. It's only now, when you sit back and think about things. I can't understand why we didn't ask more questions about him.

As I drove home, all I could think about was how we could find out about him, who I could ask for help. My mind was in complete turmoil. What if I hadn't gone to the shops today. I would never have found out about my Dad. What if... what if... I don't believe this, it's got to be fate, it's got to be. Please don't let it be too late.

After all these years was this true, my Dad was not dead? Had he just walked out on his three kids and his wife? Was it my Mam? It must have been something and I wanted to know.

I felt that I owed this to myself and no-one was going to stand in my way. No matter what the cost, I just had to find out. The only thing was time and it was against me, as I'd figured out that my Dad would be in his seventies if he was still alive.

The search was on. I'd found out most of the Millers' phone numbers in Hobart from the International Telephone Directory and rang each one. I had to wait up late as the time difference is about ten hours in front of us and had to give the people I was ringing time to get up. At least they would be thinking straight if it was mid-morning for them.

The first Miller was really nice and very surprised to get a phone call from England, but he was not the Miller I wanted.

The second Miller wanted to know if I knew their family in Kent. Now I know England is small compared to Australia, but Kent is a long way from Liverpool. They asked me about the weather and what time it was here. The phone call came to a dead end.

The next Miller was very angry, wanting to know how I'd got their phone number here in England. I tried to tell her I was looking for my Dad, his name being Ronald Gordon Miller and his age would be about early seventies. The lady put the phone down on me after saying, "No, you're wrong. He's not here! You have the wrong number."

There was something about that phone call that left me thinking for weeks, but for some reason, I couldn't bring myself to ring back in case she slammed the phone down on me again.

All the other Millers came to a dead end.

I rang the Government Archives and two national papers, but it didn't come to anything. After many phone calls and letters, I had started to get very disheartened and put it to rest. Then anger overwhelmed me as I'd given up without a fight and knew I'd never get piece of mind. How could I give up? The search was on again, but this time I started in another direction.

I began with the Coroner's Office and spoke to a nice man on the phone, who said, after I gave him all the information he needed to know, "It's Christmas and the Office will be closed for the holiday. I'll get it to you as soon as possible."

Now, opening the big brown envelope, I slowly took out its contents. It was the first time in my life that I'd ever seen a coroner's report, and didn't know what to expect. This report was to tell me all the unanswered questions I had wanted to know as a child.

My heart was in my boots. I could feel the sadness taking over me as my eyes started to fill up. It was the closest I'd been to my Mum in years, yet she was no longer here. I wanted to know right up to her last minute and what it was that made this lovely woman, my Mum, take her life.

I sat back in my chair and looked out of the window at the sky, trying to remember her the way she was, through the short memories I had.

She was tall and slim, with sharp features, always had a smile, her auburn hair fell into little curls and I can still remember the pinny she wore with a little pocket. Mum always found a penny in that pocket to give me for sweets.

Thinking about it, Mrs Williams was right, Jeanette is the spit of my Mum. The only difference being that our Jeanette has fair hair.

I lit up a cigarette and began to read.

The report had statements from people who had spoken to my Mum, each one in turn saying more or less the same, that Mum was very worried about bringing up her three children alone, and her being so very upset about my Dad not being there, also saying there was no money coming in.

If only all this was happening today and not then, there's a lot more help to be given now. Those days it was so hard to bring up three children with no money, wondering where the next meal was coming from. My Dad had gone back to sea and just never came home some three years earlier. No-one knew where he was, and his money had well stopped. Mum had written letters to shipping companies, but never got any answers.

All these things would have been playing on her mind, and maybe it was too much for her to handle. I was starting to understand – Mum must have gone to hell and back when we were little, all three of us maybe wanting this or that. It must have broken her heart, not being able to give us the things we wanted, money being so short.

I felt so sick inside. All I wanted to do was put my arms around my Mum and tell her everything's okay, give her a cuddle. I could feel her pain, her heartache, but all too late. I could say nothing or do nothing ... if only!!

My Mum had committed suicide in April 1951 by jumping off the Thurston Ferry Boat on the River Mersey. She was found eight weeks later – her body was found floating in the Sandon Dock by a Security Guard. My Nan had to go to the Coroner's Office to identify her clothes, as I don't think she would have been able to see her body after being in the water for so long.

As I read the report, I was no longer sitting there with the papers in my hand, but was a little girl of five years old. My past had all come back to me.

The highlight of the day was to play at the bottom of Solver Street and Hodson Place, bursting the tar bubbles, sometimes with a lolly-ice stick I had found or I would play hop-scotch with a stone I'd found in the gutter. My Mam would go mad seeing my hands and little cotton dress full of tar when she called me in for my tea.

"My God, you should have been a boy, it's not worth putting a clean dress on you!"

If some of the other kids were playing out, we would play hide and seek. I didn't mind that game as most of the time I'd run up the back entry into our house and be looking out the bedroom window at the kids trying to find me. They soon got wind of what I was up to and refused to let me play anymore. Ruby Appleton, who lived opposite us, was my best friend. Ruby was just three months older than me and thought she could boss me around. She always made me go for the ball when she batted it up the street.

"Go on," she'd say, with a shove, "get the ball or you're not having a go at the bat!"

When I'd got the stupid ball for her, she would go home and wouldn't lend me her bat anyway. Sometimes we would pinch an old can out of the bin just to kick it around the street. All the kids from other streets would come into our street just to play 'kick the can' until Mrs Lewis would stand on her step and start shouting: "Go on, get back in your own street! Bloody kids! Go on, sod off the lot of you!"

Her shouting always brought the other neighbours out, and if Mrs Lewis got the chance she would run up the street trying to get hold of our can to put back in the bin. If she did get it, we would get another just to annoy her.

Again, if we played two balls on the wall, she would be straight out. "Shift! Now shift and take those bloody balls with you!" she'd yell.

The more she shouted, the more we would play by her door.

"Moaning old cow! She's always the same, just

wait till she wants a message, our Joyce, don't you go."

"I won't, don't you worry!"

"And the next time she gives you any bruised apples, just throw them back at her."

"Yeah, she never gives you a penny, just old apples or sweets she's had for years. They're horrible! You can't take the paper off as its always stuck to the sweet."

"Joyce, will you go up Breck Road? Joyce, will you go the Co-Op? Joyce, will you go the butchers?" I mimicked her, waving my hands in the air.

"Okay, you don't have to go on," complained Joyce.

"Yeah, but as soon as she asks, you go. You're so stupid, just say no."

"Come on, fancy a game of rounders?" Ruby would interrupt.

"Yeah, but don't you go home with the bat."

"Look out, Mrs Lewis is at her window. Let's go and play in Hodson Place."

We ran past her house all singing 'Mrs Lewis is a moaning old cow, Mrs Lewis is a moaning old cow". Her door swung open. "That's it, I'm telling your mother on you, you cheeky little bitch, just you wait!"

"Go on then, I dare you, I taunted.

"I'll get the Police."

"Get who you like, and, anyway, my Mam's not in! So there."

"Don't you give me cheek!"

"I'm not givin' you cheek."

Pulling faces at Mrs Lewis, we ran down the street.

"That old cow is one real moaner!"

"Yeah, you watch, she'll stand on the step in a minute wanting a message. She won't ask me, I always say no."

"Well, I'm saying no, then."

"When she scrubs the step you can see her knickers."

"Urgh! What colour are they?"

"Blue, or sometimes white and they go right down to her knees, 'cos when she bends over, her big bum sticks in the air."

"Oh eh, Ruby, next time she scrubs the step, I'll have a look."

"That's what we should call her, Mrs Big Long Knickers!"

"Yeah! We will, eh!"

"Bet she wees them as well!"

"Come on, let's walk past her house singing Mrs Lewis has wet her knickers, Mrs Lewis has wet her knickers."

"Ruby, there's my Nan! Shut up, she'll give me a belt if she hears me."

"Hi, Nan."

"What have you two been up to?"

"Nothing, why?"

"Mrs Lewis said you have been givin' cheek. If I catch you givin' cheek, you're in for the day."

"She's a liar! We've just come out, we haven't seen the old cow!"

"Ya what! Don't let me hear you calling her that again!"

"Well, she is!"

"Makes no difference, and you can stop answering me back."

"I never."

"Don't start, m'lady, go on, play down the street. Your tea will be ready soon, then you're in for the night."

"Ok, Nan, give us a shout when it's ready. What is it?"

"Beans on toast."

"Oh, I hate beans, and God help our Gordon after beans! He's always fartin'! Just stinks the house out!"

"See you tomorrow, Ruby, see ya."

* * * * *

Today was different, I couldn't go out to play with the tar bubbles or play hop-scotch in the street. Our Gordon and me had been playing Mums and Dads in our back yard. We had been washing the dolls clothes in an old bowl of water and had decided to use the old mangle that was standing in our back yard against the wall by the back door.

The mangle was made of iron with two big wooden rollers and at the side was a big wheel with a handle that was far too big and heavy for me to use. That job was for the Dad and the Dad was our Gordon. I'd picked up the wet dolls clothes and put them by the wooden rollers, and before I had time to say go, our Gordon had started to turn the big wheel, trapping my fingers on my left hand.

I screamed as the blood splashed against the white washed wall behind the mangle and was running down the wooden rollers that was supposed to wring out the doll's clothes. Mam ran out of the back kitchen door and picked me up in her arms. She ran me into the back kitchen and put my hand under the tap. I could see the water turn red against the white stone sink.

My two fingers had split open at the top and the pain was like nothing I had felt before. I wanted to faint and felt so sick. Mam was crying as well, and turning to me Nan said: "Take care of these two, I'll have to run her to Mill Road Hospital."

Our Jeanette and Gordon were both upset, but not as much as I was at the thought of going to the hospital. I cried all the way there and all the way back. The Nurse hurt me looking for splinters from the old wooden rollers and trying to clean the splits. With my hand all bandaged up I was told to keep it clean, so it stopped me from playing with the tar bubbles ... for a week or so anyway.

3

Just before I was due to go back to the hospital for
the all-clear, my Nan got me washed and dressed
quickly and before I could understand what was
going on, took me to the Police Station. As we
walked in, we could see a tall man standing behind
the desk talking to a man and woman. The tall
policeman had a big, fat, red face and big hands. I
couldn't take my eyes off him, his hands they were
so big.

We sat down and waited our turn until the man
and woman had finished and walked out. My Nan
told me to stay there and wait while she walked over
and talked to the policeman. I couldn't remember
doing anything wrong, so why had she brought me
here. Our Jeanette and Gordon had gone to school

and that's where I should be. Only for my hand I would have gone as well, so it's not my fault.

I thought the policeman would have told me off, but he stayed behind the desk talking to my Nan. I heard Nan saying that her daughter hadn't come home and she never stayed out. Getting a piece of paper from behind the desk, the policeman asked Nan some more questions.

"How old is she?"

"Twenty five," Nan said.

"Do you know what she was wearing?"

"Yes, a green coat, blue blouse, black skirt and black peep toe shoes."

Just then two policemen walked into the Police Station, one of them put his hand on my head, ruffled my hair and winked at me. I could hear the policeman behind the desk ask Nan if Mam was married.

"Yes, she has three children and that's her youngest," turning around and pointing at me. "Jeanette is the oldest, she's nine, then there's Gordon, he's seven, then Joyce here, who's five."

"What about her husband?"

I never heard Nan's answer. As the door opened a man walked in. Under his coat I could see a small black puppy, his little head sticking out. As he sat down next to me, he didn't put the puppy down on the floor as it was dirty. It had sweet papers and cigarette stumps all over it. Turning to me the man said: "Do you want a dog?"

Nan heard and swung around. "No, he doesn't, we have enough mouths to feed."

Taking my hand, Nan walked out of the door. I was glad to get out into the busy street and still didn't know why we had to go there and soon forgot about the little black puppy, being too busy holding on to my Nan's skirt as we made our way home.

As the weeks went by, we stopped asking Nan about our Mam as the answer was always the same, "I don't know so stop asking. I don't know."

The last week in June we had come home from school to find Nan crying. The neighbours had been in and out of our house all day and we were told to go out and play. Our Jeanette took me by the hand and walked me into the back kitchen saying, "I think they've found Mam."

"Where is she? Is she coming home then?"

"Shh, I'll tell you later, now be quiet and go upstairs."

"Why? Is she up there?"

"No, just go upstairs."

I did as our Jeanette asked and waited to be told. If my Mam was found then why was my Nan and our Jeanette so upset?

Our Gordon hadn't come in from school yet. He was always late, but I bet he knew, he always knew before me. I sat on the bed waiting for our Jeanette to come upstairs to me. The bedroom was big, in it was a big bed that me and our Jeanette slept in and on the other side of the room was a small bed that our Gordon slept in. Between the beds was a chest of drawers that had handles on that looked like faces. When it was dark, I tried not to look at them.

The walls were painted green and the oil cloth on the floor was nearly the same colour and between the two beds was a rug made out of bits of cloth. They were called 'clipper rugs'. Most houses had them as they were home made from sacks and strips of cloth about five inches long by one inch wide. A needle with a hook was used to pull the cloth through the sack, then it was tied off.

If you were posh you made a nice pattern with the cloth, ours was just plain. Over our Gordon's bed was a gas mantle with a chain and a small ring at the end. The window was big, my Mam and Nan used to sit on the window ledge to clean the outside window and would shut the window down on their legs to stop them from falling out.

The bedroom door opened and in walked our Gordon. He was crying and threw himself on the bed. So he did know what was going on then, they all did except me. Our Jeanette came into the room and sat on the bed next to me. She put her arm around me, and with tears running down her face, told me that our Mam was dead. Like Gordon and Jeanette, my tears ran uncontrollable until sleep took away the pain and hurt we all felt.

On the day of our Mam's funeral, we had to go to school as all three of us were too young to attend. We never did say our goodbyes, she had gone, never to return. It was a stigma in those days to commit suicide and we paid the price. Kids at school shouted horrible things at us and the kids in the street were just as bad.

"Your Mam's dead and you've got no Dad!"

The 'Dad' bit never bothered me as I didn't know what a Dad was. I'd seen one, but I didn't know what they were for or what they did, so it never worried me what they shouted. When they said horrible things about my Mam, though, it made me cry and I would run home to my Nan.

The next few weeks took their toll on us all, especially Nan. She never did have rosy cheeks, but now she looked yellow, very drawn, and seemed to be in pain, more so than the last week. Her thin frame looked even thinner and it wasn't long before she asked our Jeanette to go for the next door neighbour, Mrs Baker.

Mrs Baker told us to stay downstairs, while she went up to look at Nan. "Jeanette, watch these two will you, I'll have to go up Breck Road to ring an ambulance, your Nan looks terrible, I think its her ulcer, she's in a lot of pain."

"Will I be okay to take a cup of tea up?"

"I don't think she'll drink it Jeanette, but you can try."

"Jeanette, what's an ulcer?"

"I don't really know. Now you two go back in the kitchen and try to be quiet. Gordon you stay in, tell your mates you will see them later."

Mrs Baker was soon back from Breck Road. "Did your Nan have a cuppa, Jeanette?"

"No, she said she wanted to be sick, so I've taken the bucket up."

"Well, don't worry, the ambulance won't be long. Listen, I'll just nip back home. I won't be a minute."

"Jeanette, who's going to look after us then?"

Jeanette didn't answer, but she looked like she was about to burst out crying.

"What's up with you?"

"Shut up, Gordon, mind your own business."

The ambulance came and took her away and we were left on our own with no-one to take care of us. One of our neighbours must have told the Social

Services that we were on our own, because a big black car stopped outside our house, and there was a 'ran-tan-tan' on the door. I could hear our Jeanette talking to someone and the next thing two big men walked in and stood there looking around our kitchen.

It was only small. It had a table with two wooden chairs, a small couch that was in the middle of the room with an armchair each side. Behind the couch was a sideboard and on the sideboard stood a big chalk alsation dog that stood on its own stand and the stand was painted to look like grass. It had chips out of it through wear and tear. To each side of the alsation was a small candle stick with no candles in them!

The two big men stood between the sideboard and the couch and told us to get our coats on. One of the men went into the back kitchen to lock the door. "Come on, get yourself ready," the taller of the men said, trying to fasten the one button on my coat. I'd lost the other two.

These men frightened us, we didn't like them, they never smiled and looked so official standing there in their long black overcoats. The taller one picked me up – that put the 'wind of God' up me and being the smallest of the three began to scream and kick out.

"Jeanette! Tell him to put me down! Tell him. It was that Mrs Baker, she told the men to take us when she rang the ambulance. I hate her!"

"Well, she could have told me what she was up to. She didn't even ask what we wanted, she just did it!"

The older of the two men told me to be quiet and keep my legs still.

"Will you stop telling her to be quiet, she's scared stiff."

Jeanette tried hard to stick up for us against the men, but to no good. They shut our front door and put us in the back of their car.

Some of our neighbours were standing by the car with their arms folded, wearing turbans on their heads. They just tutted and shook their heads, they could see that we were crying, they could have taken us in. We wouldn't have eaten much and would have been good. Too late to even ask, the car drove off down the street, where to we didn't know.

Our Jeanette trying to be brave said, "Don't worry, we'll be okay."

I'd never been in a car before and it took a long time to get there. What was this place? We could see it was a very big building as the car drove through the gates. It was dark and all the windows were bright with the light. The car came to a stand still and the men carried me out and into the building. It was Olive Mount Orphanage.

It was very bright inside and before we knew what was happening, I was put into a big bath. The water was very hot and made my legs and bum go red. As I tried to sit down in this big deep bath, I noticed that the water smelt just like the stuff my Mam used to use to wash the floor in our back kitchen.

The room was tiled from floor to ceiling with white tiles. On the wall, the other side of the bath was a sink with two dull taps and behind me a big window with no curtains. I couldn't see out of the window for the mist and water droplets running in straight lines right down to a dirty window ledge. At the bottom of the bath, the tiles had cracked and some had fell off the wall. By the door was a chair painted red and on it I'd put my clothes.

Under the chair on the floor was my shoes with my socks in each, my Mam showed me how to do that so I wouldn't lose them.

With turning around to look at the room, I'd lost the block of white soap in the bath. The bath was big, it could take about five kids in it, but I had it all to myself and no chance of finding the soap. My Nan never put this smell in our bath – what was it for anyway? How could this funny smell make me clean? Only the soap could do that and I'd lost it. The water was too hot for me to move around and being frightened I just sat there.

The door of the bathroom opened and in walked a woman. She was very thin with short hair going grey and wearing dark rimmed glasses.

"Come on, let's get you out," she said.

Lifting me out of the hot water, I stood on a white towel with words across the top in blue. The towel she gave me was hard and I found it not very good to dry myself. When I was dry, she handed me a stiff white nightie that also had the same blue words in a circle on the left hand shoulder.

Taking me by the hand, she took me downstairs to a large room where our Jeanette was sitting on a chair, with her elbows leaning against the table and her face in her hands. She looked up at me and gave me a little smile. I don't know what was going on, but like me she was still very upset.

I was told to stand on a stool were the thin woman started to look me over, first down my mouth, then my ears, turning my head this way and that, then she was looking through my hair, paying special attention to the back of my ears. Holding on to my long brown hair that used to fall into ringlets when wet, she said: "This will have to go."

"Oh no, don't cut my hair! Jeanette, don't let

them cut my hair!"

I tried so hard to pull away from her grip. I used to love my Mam brushing my hair and would sit there while she told me a story. All this woman wanted to do was cut it off. The woman stood behind me with a big pair of scissors and I could hear snip, snip, snip.

Through the tears, I could see long strands of my hair falling on the floor and I knew the red scotch ribbon in my hand would never go back in my hair again. The horrible woman had hacked my hair good and proper and my fringe was like steps; the back of my hair had long bits and short bits.

"My God, what have you done?" said our Jeanette as she stood up from the chair and walked around me. Fighting back her tears and trying so hard to be brave she said, "Don't worry, Joyce, it'll grow, it's okay, I'll look after you, they won't hurt you, not while I'm here."

The bedroom was very big and I could see by the light from the corridor that it had about twenty or so beds and I could see someone in all but two of them. These must have been for our Jeanette and me. Between each bed was a small cabinet, but I noticed that there was not one thing on the top of any of them, no brush or comb or a little doll or teddy.

The room was full, yet empty of anyone's belongings, not even shoes under the beds.

I always put my shoes under the bed, but not these girls. The bedroom was so neat and clean, it didn't feel right. The big windows around the room had no curtains. We had curtains on our bedroom windows at home that Nan shut each night.

As I tried to look round the room, I could see a dark head on each pillow, it must be very late as it was very quiet and all the girls looked fast asleep, not one of them moved.

The only sound came from downstairs. I could hear voices and then a door shut. Thank God they had forgot to put the landing light out. The light that shone through the half closed door was still enough for me to see more of the bedroom. The far end of the room looked the same as this end, all neat and tidy, not one picture on the walls. I didn't like this room, I wanted to go home.

As I lay there, the stars were bright in the sky, but one star was the brightest of all and that was my Mam looking down on me, I knew it was her.

The girl in the next bed was awake and had seen me come in and as soon as the woman walked out of the bedroom, she sat up. "What's your name?"

"Joyce."

"What time did you come in?"

"I don't know."

I couldn't tell the time, but it was dark so I knew it was late. We had been talking for a few minutes when one of the older girls walked in. "You and you, get downstairs".

We both had our backsides slapped hard. I didn't know we were not allowed to talk once in bed. No one had bothered to tell me. I learned the hard way about all the rules over the next few weeks. It was always a slap on the back of the legs or being shaken until my head nearly fell off my shoulders.

4

After about five or six weeks we were transferred to Fazakerly Cottage Homes on the other side of Liverpool.

Either they had the same rules or some of the girls like us had also been transferred, because we could see a lot of girls with no hair. What happened was, if you came into an orphanage with nits, they never bothered to clean your hair, just shaved the lot off. Quite a few had no hair or very little, about an inch long. It was bad enough mine being cut, but to have it shaved would really upset me. I must have had no nits.

Me and our Jeanette were told to sit down and wait on the chairs in the hall. Our house could have fitted in this hall, it was so big with a staircase that must have had a thousand stairs and been wide enough for three or four girls to walk up side by side. I would love the chance to slide down the banister. In the hall was four doors, all closed and behind one I could hear pots and pans and smell food that was being cooked.

The door to the office opened and out walked a big fat woman, her name was Mrs Brown. She wore dark clothes and on her feet, shoes that were too big and worn down on the heel as she shuffled around. In her hair she had pins to keep the curls in place and she spoke very sternly with no smile, "You call me Mother from now on, take your things upstairs."

Looking past us she pointed to a girl coming down the stairs, "Margaret will show you the way."

Jeanette and me stood up, picked up our little bags then started to walk up the big staircase towards Margaret who was waiting for us to catch up to her. Turning to our Jeanette I said, "See, she had nits."

Our Gordon fell on his feet, the Cottage he was to stay in looked after him very well. However, unlike our Gordon, we never got a sweet ration. Mrs Brown would only give us three or four sweets a week, while our Gordon got a whole unopened bag. Mrs Brown not only took our sweets, but was seen more than once taking eggs, sugar and fruit.

From day one we hated it and hated the woman who tried to get us to call her Mother, all the more. Mrs Brown was very cruel, not only to me, but to the other girls as well. If your face didn't fit then God help you, she made your life hell one way or another. In the morning we had porridge for breakfast – and porridge is one food I hate, no way would I eat it. This white thick slop in the bowl made my stomach turn so I just couldn't eat it. Mrs Brown stood over me, "Eat it, come, on eat it!" she shouted.

All the shouting didn't help, I left the porridge and went to school.

The first day at the new school was a nightmare, we had to dress in a long gymslip that was far too big and we had to tie the belt tight so that the gymslip could be pulled up, it never looked right. We had black stockings to wear, but were not given anything to keep them up with. We found the best way was to tie a huge knot at the top to try to keep them up. The shoes were black with a silver buckle on that was broken and I stepped out of them all the way to school, as they were a size too big! I had cursed the girl who had worn them before me for not taking care of them.

The school was called Lambeth Square, a small school made of wood. It was situated at the top of

Townsend Avenue by the East Lancashire Road. As we got off the bus to go into our new school, down fell the stockings! After pulling them back up, turning to Jeanette, I said, "Oh, what am I going to do, these stockings keep falling down. That's it, I'm not goin' to school!"

Jeanette bent down and tried to show me how to put a knot in the top of the stockings. "Joyce, look what I'm doing, then you can do it if they fall again."

"Oye! Jeanette, that hurt!"

"Well, keep still. That's it. How does that feel?"

"That's okay now. If they fall down again, I'm goin' home."

"Joyce, you can't go home."

"Then I'll just sit outside till you all come out."

"Come on, don't be stupid, you know how to do the knots now, you'll be okay."

I had to hold on to the knots through the gymslip. I must have walked into school like a soldier and those stupid stockings stopped me from playing out at playtime for fear of them falling down. I never did get to grips with those stockings.

All the kids dressed the same from the orphanage and could be picked out a mile away and didn't the kids at school skit. They said cruel things like, "Poor kids," and, "Was your Mam and Dad dead or was you dumped?"

Well, that was the first day over, not that I was going to learn anything as the teacher thought it was a waste of time to teach you anything as you may not be staying long. I was given a book and told to sit at the back of the class and that was my schooling.

Back at the Cottage I was more than ready for our tea before going to bed. I was starving and the smell from the kitchen made me twice as hungry. I got washed and changed out of the horrible school clothes and made my way down to the dining room and sat down. Each girl was given their tea – sausages, mashed potato and vegetables.

To my horror, in front of me was the bowl of porridge from that morning which had gone hard on top. At the end of the meal the girls could leave the table, but I had to stay. Mrs Brown told me that I could only leave once I had eaten the porridge. After about half an hour with the bowl of porridge still in front of me, I was told to go to bed.

The next day was just the same, but at the end of tea time, Mrs Brown could see that I had dug my heels in hard. The porridge was put into the bin. I had won and it was worth going without just to see her face. I was never given porridge again. I hated this woman, a feeling that I'd never felt before, it came from deep inside of me and would not move.

Me and our Jeanette wanted to run away from this place and the fat woman Mrs Brown, but how? We had nowhere to go, no money, no Mam's arms to run back to. Oh, Mam, we missed you.

The weeks passed and our talk of running away was strong. It had been snowing hard and was freezing as we got on the bus to school. The bus was full of kids, so me and our Jeanette had to go upstairs. We had made up our minds, it was today or never to run away. We saw our Gordon get off the bus and banged hard on the windows to try and catch his attention, but it was too late, the bus moved away from the stop and our Gordon walked into his school without hearing or seeing us.

The bus was full of people, kids going to other schools and the grown ups off to work or early shopping with the weather being so bad.

It was hard trying to see out the window with the outside dirt and snow, and the inside steam from all the peoples breaths. No matter how many times we wiped the window the steam came back, making it hard to see which way the bus was going. We had never been this far away from home on our own and didn't have a clue if the bus was even going anywhere near our house.

"Now keep quiet Joyce. If the inspector gets on

the bus, get ready to jump off, just in case he reports us. If you see anywhere that you know, tell me, okay?"

The bus floor was soaking wet with the melted snow people had brought on under their shoes and the workman who had just stood up to get off the bus must have had big boots on. There was black slush on the floor where he had sat.

"Joyce, will you keep looking out the window not around the bus! We should be close now, we've been on this bus for ages."

"Change seats, Jeanette, and you look out. I'm freezing sitting here and this stupid window won't shut properly. The wind is blowing right down my ear!"

"Will you be quiet, people are looking at us, just shut up and look out the window."

"Ha! That man has just gone flying on his bum!"

"It's not funny, Joyce, he could have hurt himself."

"Na, I don't think so, he got up too quickly. Bet he feels ashamed."

"Come on, the next stop is ours."

"How do you know?"

" 'Cos that man fell outside the Royal, so the next stop is ours. Now, watch the stairs or you might end up on your bum!"

Our Jeanette held my hand all the way home. We got off the bus on Breck Road at the top of Solver Street. We had to walk out into the road as a big piece of snow was hanging off a roof and was ready to fall off. Some snow had already fallen and the people who lived in the house had brushed it into the gutter.

The snow was high into the gutter and the bus had to drive in the middle of the road, which was slushy and dirty and the tyres had made their mark.

Not being dressed for the winter snow, we were soon frozen to the bone. As we made our way down our street we saw an ambulance drive away from our house. Our Jeanette grabbed my arm, bringing me to a stand still. Please God, let it be Nan. As we ran down the street our Nan opened the door, she looked so pale and thin. The house was a total mess.

While Nan had been in hospital, the house had been robbed and smashed up. What little we had, they had taken. What they couldn't take was slashed, including the beds. We stood looking at the room with tears running down our faces, why had someone done this to us?

"Nan, who did this to us? Mrs Baker was supposed to have the key, why didn't she look after our house?"

"Jeanette, I don't know. I haven't seen her yet."

"Some friend she turned out to be."

"Nan, she told the men to come for us and she didn't tell our Jeanette."

"Don't worry about that now. Will you help pick up those records and watch you don't cut yourself."

"Jeanette, get the bucket from the yard for Joyce to put these records in. I see they took the ones they wanted, but why smash the rest? Doesn't make sense."

"Oh Nan, look what's missing, Les Paul, Rosemary Cloony and all your Billy Ekstine records."

"Jeanette, just get the bucket, love. I don't feel too good. Joyce, start clearing this mess up."

The house was freezing, it was colder inside than out. Nan cried when our Jeanette came in from the back yard saying they had even taken the coal, what was left would never make a fire. Nan got up slowly from the chair and started to look in the cupboard at the side of the big black grate for old shoes to burn, as we rolled the old Echos up tight, then twist into rings to help make a fire.

"Go over the road, Joyce, and ask Mrs Lewis to lend me ten bob. I know she's in because she was standing by the door when the ambulance brought me home and we might see a coal man to get coal," said Nan.

Putting my wet shoes back on and not even bothering to fix the broken buckle, I walked across the street.

Mrs Lewis' house was posh, she had nice lace curtains on her window and a lovely brass knob on her brown door. Her step had gone in at the middle as she was always scrubbing it and she had left her mark on the edge of her step by using a sand stone. I was blowing my hot breath into my hands to keep them warm and started to stamp my feet. My toes had gone numb. The door opened and Mrs Lewis stood in front of me, a big bonny lady with grey hair who always wore a full apron, her arms folded under her large chest.

I tried to tell her what Nan wanted, but before I could finish, Mrs. Lewis said, "Tell your Nan I neither borrow nor lend," and shut the door.

Our Jeanette shouted from the back kitchen, "Nan, there's no milk, will you have 'cony-ony' instead?" Nan's eyes filled up again as I told her what Mrs. Lewis had said.

"Nan, she said tell your Nan I don't borrow or lend."

"Oh, I don't believe that Mrs Lewis, she knows the way things are. It's all right for her, what with her husband and two sons working, she's got a few bob that one."

"Well, that's the last message I do for her."

"Stuck up cow!" said our Jeanette passing Nan a cup of tea. The shoes Nan were burning gave off an awful smell of rubber, but at least the room was getting warmer.

"Nan, I could smell scouse when she opened the door, I'm starving now."

"Joyce, I think I've got half a crown at the back of my purse. Put your coat back on and go up the chippy."

"Joyce, ask for loads of salt and vinegar."

"Nan, what do you want? Do you fancy a fish cake or what?"

"No, just get something for Jeanette and you. I feel lousy, must be this place, it's put me off food. Get a small loaf and half pound of marg as well, but go for the bread and marg first, or the chips will be cold by the time you get back. Mind you don't slip."

The day flew over and it started to go dark. Nan had found a candle to light up the room that was neither use nor ornament. There was a loud knock on the door, the same two big men who had come once before, were again standing in our kitchen. They had come to take us back. The school had reported to the orphanage that we did not turn up for school.

"What's going on, what do you want?"

Nan told the two men she wanted us to stay, but looking around the kitchen Nan knew we had to go back.

I looked across the room at our Jeanette, and knew she was just as upset as I was. "Oh Nan, please don't send us back, please, we'll be okay, we'll be good."

I sat by Jeanette, if she stayed, I stayed. Nan wouldn't send me back on my own, but she might want Jeanette here to help her tidy up.

"Nan, I'll tidy up for you, can we stay please?"

The tears started to flow, and turning round to look at our Jeanette I saw she was the same, but she didn't make a sound, the tears just ran down her face and fell off the end of her chin onto her hands. Standing up from her chair Nan told me to get my coat on, it was no good we had to go back.

We could hear Nan talking to the two men about the house all smashed up when she came home. It was like talking to the wall, her words fell on deaf ears, all they wanted was to take us back.

Nan had started to pick up over the day, but not now, she was just as upset as us and it showed. She told us not to worry.

"When I get the house fixed up, you can all come home, it'll take time to get new beds and coal, but I will come back for you, don't cry, I will bring you home, I promise."

Giving our Nan a love and a kiss we left with the men, but this time I walked out. At six years of age I thought I was too old to be carried out.

5

Yes, we were back at the same Cottage and who was waiting at the door, but enemy number one, Mrs Brown.

"Hello girls," she sounded so pleased, but that was because the two men were standing there. Once inside it was like we were never away, was it a dream? No, it wasn't a dream, it was true, we did run away and we were going to pay for each lousy minute.

Jeanette was given her jobs to do, mine was to scrub a room, then with a tin of polish that was far too big to fit in my hand and a cloth to try and put a shine on the wooden floor. Running away was smashing while it lasted and the thought of my Nan and our house kept me going until the floor was finished. Mrs Brown came into the room to inspect my work. Looking down at me on my knees with a cold stare she made my blood run cold.

"And if you don't do it properly, you do it again."

"I hate you! I hate you! I'll tell my Nan on you!"

All I could see was the door slamming behind her. The room took me hours and I was glad to get to bed, only to be woken up by wetting the bed again. I tried to sleep on the edge of the bed where it was dry, but it was no good as my pyjamas were wet right up my back and it felt cold.

Next morning I cried, "Jeanette, I've wet the bed again, oh, Jeanette, what am I going to do?"

"Joyce, don't worry, we'll swap the top sheet and put it on the bottom."

I watched our Jeanette do the bed again for me, she hid the round patch and nothing was said, so we got away with it.

Another job I hated was peeling potatoes, I'd sit on the back step with a big pan on the right, a sack of potatoes on the left and a small bin to take the peelings in the middle. Once the pan was full, I'd take it into the kitchen for the cook. The cook would wash the potatoes and say if she wanted any more and she always found time to look through the peelings, if any were too thick you always felt a sting on your face with her hand. It was her way of teaching you.

I hated her just as much as Mrs Brown. She was a small woman, but bonny, always wore a white apron which stayed clean because the girls did the work for her. Other girls had their jobs to do, washing up, scrubbing the table, brushing the floor.

The kitchen was very big. On the stove I could see big black pans with lots of steam coming from them and the smell of food filled the room. Against the wall was a big white sink, a lot bigger than the one at home. It was that big it could be used for a bath and it was just as deep.

At the side of the sink was a wooden draining board with dishes on waiting to be dried and put away. Above the sink were two taps that came out of the wall, but the girls found them hard to turn on, and had to use both hands just for one tap, while trying to balance on the small wooden stool in case they fell in, jobs bigger girls should be doing, not the little ones.

Big brown handled knives lay on the table for the cook to use, and a big pastry board that was still being used was also on the table. At the side of the board was a big stone pot that the cook kept her flour in.

The sound of girls talking and laughing stopped

when a girl the other side of the kitchen dropped a plate. She knew and we knew what was to come next. The cook looked over at the girl, then the floor. The slap on the girl's face echoed across the kitchen. No-one spoke, not even the girl, who had a large red mark on the left side of her face. She, like the rest of us, tried never to cry.

The cook had that slap right down to a fine art. The work in the kitchen carried on. We spoke with our eyes, never saying a word. All the girls hated the cook, I wasn't on my own there.

The only person I liked was Mrs Johnson, a small timid woman who wore glasses and spoke with a quiet voice. She used to show me how to darn socks and because I liked her, I tried to please. If you couldn't thread a needle because of the fluff at the end of the wool, she would wink at me, saying, "I'll show you a little trick," and would wet the end so the wool would go through the eye of the needle.

"There you go, now you try it."

Mrs Johnson was nice. If Mrs Brown was about and having a go at one of the girls, Mrs Johnson would look at one of us, then go gozzy to make us laugh. Mrs Brown never found out what started us all off, and the more we laughed the more Mrs Johnson pulled the faces.

I wanted to tell Mrs Johnson about the cook and

Mrs Brown, about the way they treated us and the way each girl hated them. Although I liked her, I still didn't feel I could trust her, just in case she went back and told them. If she did tell them then God help you, so no-one said a word for fear of them, it wasn't worth it.

Our Jeanette and me had been there for months. Just how long was it going to take before we could go home again? Nan had said months ago it wouldn't be long, but it had been long. We just wanted to go home. I could see me and our Jeanette running away again if our Nan didn't come soon. But, it was no sooner said than done, because Mrs Brown came up to us and said, "Next week you two are off home. Your Nan's been on the phone."

"What did she say?" we asked excitedly.

"All she said was that she was coming next Saturday for you."

"What about our Gordon?"

"He will be going as well."

The following week dragged by, all we could think about was going home. Girls older than us were sent to London to go into Service when they reached fifteen, and some kids were sent to Australia, so thank God Nan was coming for us, or we might have ended up in London, then how would she find us and how would we get back home. I didn't even know where London or Australia was – our Jeanette said that it was very far away.

"Nan, don't let us go back there," we begged, when Saturday finally arrived, "you don't know what it's like, they hate us."

"Don't worry now, just get your things and lets get you all home."

Back home the house seemed very small and quiet, Nan had worked hard to get it ship-shape and she even had colour in her face. We felt like rabbits in the field, wanting to kick up our heels. We were so happy to be home and in our own beds, new ones at that.

The big alsation dog had gone, it had been broken when our house had been smashed up. Nan had tried to glue it all back, but it was never the same, so she put it in the bin. The two candle sticks were still there, but between them now was a small wooden clock that chimed on the hour. All three sat on a nice lace cloth. The couch had nice new cushion covers on, the same as the chairs.

The big black grate was nice and clean, and the

small line Nan put under the mantle had a nice clean tea towel hanging from it which she used to take fresh baked scones out of the oven at the side of the fire. It was a nice smell, and those scones where the best we've ever tasted.

"Do you fancy some 'fin an' addy' for your tea?" Nan said looking around at our little faces.

"That would be nice Nan, put a knob of marg on the top."

"Now, I've got a nice brown loaf to go with it. Joyce, you set the table. Gordon, you get a shovel of coal and Jeanette, you take those bags upstairs and I'll put the 'fin an' addy' on the pan and make us all a nice cup of tea."

Gordon dropped some coal on the way across the kitchen off the shovel, he stopped and looked up at Nan.

"Don't worry, it's okay, just pick it up," said Nan.

Our Gordon smiled, he also knew from now on things were going to be great.

After tea I was glad when Ruby called for me to go out. The house stunk of fish, even with the back door open the smell didn't move.

"Fancy a game of hop-scotch?"

"No, but if you still have that bat we'll play rounders."

"With just the two of us? That's no good."

"Well, let's give Barbara a knock, she might play."

"Yeah, but that's only three of us, still not enough."

"Okay, what about Joan next door?"

"She's gone to her aunties."

"Oh come on, what else do you want to play then. You'll have to hurry up or I'm goin' in."

"Tell you what, I'll get my rope out, but come round the back, Nan's having a sleep."

I ran in and came out more subdued, "Ruby, Nan said I've got to stay in, that's your fault."

"How is that my fault?"

"You should have got the bat out."

"Oh Joyce, ask her if you can sit on the front step, go on."

"Nan, can we just play on the front step for an hour?"

"You go away from that door and you're in for the week. I want you in at six and no later."

"Tell you what Joyce, your Nan never changes does she?"

We spent the next hour talking about all the things I'd missed out on while I'd been away. I was glad to go in as I wanted to try out the new bed, and be able to have a good lie-in in the morning.

There were nice clean sheets on the bed, and the bedroom looked lovely, the little home-made mat had gone, and a nice red runner was in its place, and on our new bed was my panda. I'd forgotten all about him, and Nan had sewn his eye back on and she'd even found a pink ribbon and put it round his neck, he looked lovely.

Our Jeanette's panda was the same colour as mine, brown, and our Gordon's was black and white. Gordon used to kick mine round the bedroom just to annoy me, or to make me cry. No wonder he lost his eye. Let him do it again and I'll batter him. I'll throw his over the back yard wall, so he'd better keep his hands to himself, I thought.

Ruby also lived with her Nan, just like us. We used to play in our back yard unless my Nan was doing the washing, which meant she needed the yard to hang out all the sheets. In that case we would go over to Ruby's back yard to play. Even though Ruby lived with her Nan I thought she was posh, her back yard was white washed and the back door was painted red and around the bottom of the walls was a red border. What made her 'lav' posh was that they had their squares of Echo on a string, while ours was on a six inch nail. Yes, Ruby was posh.

Saturday was always bath night. Nan would

bring the big tin bath from the back yard and put it in the back kitchen by the fire. The pans on the stove were full of water on the boil. Each in turn would have our bath, using the same water of course, but being the youngest, I always had my bath last. If our Gordon came in looking like the ace of spades, the water would be like mud.

Nan used a block of soap called 'durback' soap, it was black and smelt just like disinfectant. Then she would go through our hair with the nit comb, although she never found any. Then when she had finished, gave us a tablespoon of cod liver oil. I hated the stuff.

"It'll do you the world of good," she would say. I don't think it did as it always made me go to the lav! Whoever was the first to go always had to take last night's Echo, so you had something to do. We would have to rip the paper into squares then one at a time put the paper on our six inch nail, until it was full, but if I had had a fight with our Gordon, I would slip the 'tit bits' magazine between the Echo so no-one would see it.

Now the 'tit bits' was a glossy magazine, and it was just what I wanted for my Saturday night job. Once down the lav, I would do a square of the Echo then a square of the glossy magazine, a square of the Echo, a square of the magazine. Now let's see you try and wipe your bum on that, and if our Gordon is the next one to go down the lav, I'll have to blow the night light out, or he will see what I've been up to. Nan will have a fit, then I'll have to do it properly and that's after our Gordon's given me a belt.

Only for the smell, I'd love to be a fly on the wall, just to see his face trying to use the paper and if he uses too much it will block the lav, as glossy paper doesn't flush very well. If that happens, never mind our Gordon, Nan will batter me.

I'd made a little friend while down there, a spider who'd made a web in the corner by the door, but our Gordon found out about it and the next time I went to the lav, it was splattered up the wall. Our Gordon had put his foot on it just to upset me.

In the winter months, Nan would put a night light out there, not just to be able to see, but to stop the pipes from freezing up and it worked as long as the door was kept shut. The seat was a square of wood with a hole in the middle that got scrubbed white with bleach twice a week, and if the last person using it splashed the seat, we would put a piece of paper there to stop you sitting on wet wood.

Our lav was at the bottom of the back yard, so each night we used to take a chamber pot to bed and each morning it had to be emptied and disinfectant put in. When we opened the back bedroom curtains, the window looked out onto the neighbours yards and we often saw them walking down their back yards to empty their chambers, they thought nobody had seen them, but I bet they could see us doing the same.

Life was just back to normal when, to our horror, Nan fell ill again.

We could not believe it when we found ourselves outside Cottage Six again, me and our Jeanette.

Gordon was the lucky one again. He was put in the same one he had been in before. Mrs Brown, the cook and Mrs Johnson were all here, the same rotten lot. The only good think that came out of this visit was we got to go on holiday to the Isle of Man. We were all given new clothes to go in and nice new shoes that no-one else had worn.

A big bus arrived at the home to take all the kids down to the Pier Head to get the boat. Nearly a full scale fight broke out on who was to sit on the back seat, but Mrs Brown only had to get on the bus and stare at us all to make us find an empty seat anywhere.

Me and our Jeanette wanted the bus to go down Breck Road, just to look at our street, but we didn't recognise anywhere the bus was going.

"Come on Joyce, lets make the best of it, it's our first holiday."

"I know, I know, but Jeanette I still feel sad. I wish the bus was taking us home instead."

The boat was full of kids, all running around and trying to stay away from Mrs Brown's evil eyes. Me and our Jeanette made our way to the top of the boat. The journey took ages to get to the Isle of Man. I wasn't too happy about not seeing any land for so long.

"What would you do if the boat went down?"

"Shut up, Joyce, trust you to say that."

"Well what would you do, would you save our Gordon and me?"

"Only myself, so shut up and let's see if we can find him, we haven't seen Gordon for ages."

"There he is, look down there."

"Where?"

"There. Talking to that red head."

"Now stop it, don't start."

"Don't start bossing me about, I'm on my holidays."

"Well, just behave yourself then."

"Our Gordon's got a butty, wonder where he got

that?"

"Well, if you move yourself, we'll get one. Come on!"

All the kids were lined up waiting for their dinner. Two ladies were standing behind two big tables giving food out to the kids. On the table was sausage rolls, butties, apples, packets of sweets and a large jug full of orange juice, with rows of paper cups.

"Joyce, I feel like Oliver Twist."

"So do I – who's Oliver Twist? Is he on the boat?"

"Oh, shut up!"

"All those butties are starting to turn up, don't take the top one. Oh, it's okay, that kid's taken it."

"Excuse me, just one apple each, put one back please."

"One's for our Jeanette."

"She's got one, put it back."

"Joyce, put it back, you can have mine if you want it."

"Miss, that kid's just taken two apples."

"Joyce, will you move away from the table!"

"Well, how come she never said anything to that kid?"

"She didn't see him, she was too busy telling you off."

When we got back to the top of the boat, two kids had pinched our seat and wouldn't move up. I don't think our Jeanette wanted to say anything, they looked too hard and told us to beat it.

"That's your fault, if you'd moved yourself we could have sat there."

"It's not my fault."

"It is!"

"Well go on, Jeanette, hit her, go on."

"Just shut up will you and look at the colour of your hands, they're black."

"I'm fed up, you telling me off all the time. I'm going to find our Gordon."

"Get back here, just wait. I'll go with you."

"No, I'm goin' myself."

"Joyce, get back here, you'll get lost. Come on, I'm sorry."

We walked up and down that boat for ages looking for our Gordon, and when we found him, he didn't want to know.

"Gordon, we've got to stay together, okay."

"I'm alright, I'm with my mates."

"Well, all stay together you lot, we'll be there soon."

We stayed at a boarding house in Douglas, which was situated up on a hill, so we had about thirty steps to climb to get to the door. With having to carry our own bags, we wished we had got the boarding house at the bottom of the hill, instead our Gordon got that one. He always falls on his feet, and his bags aren't even as heavy as ours!

"How come our Gordon got that house?"

"Because all the lads are in that one and all the girls are in this one. Will you stop moaning. That's all you've done all day."

"Bossy boots!"

"I heard that! Look, don't start. All I've heard all day is you moaning."

I was starving, tired, fed up and the boat had made me feel sick, rocking from side to side, and that stupid lad didn't help. He was sick all over the place – peas, carrots, the lot came up and splashed all over my new best shoes and on my foot. All our Jeanette did was tell me off for being so close to the lad. I didn't know he was going to throw up. Well, I hope we don't have any peas or carrots for tea, if we do, I'm going to look under the table to see who's got new shoes on and see how they feel, yuk!

The boarding house was posh with nice chairs and tables and being high up gave us a really nice view over the bay. We could see all the boats coming and going and we would watch the tide turn as the day goes on. One day a bus came and took us to visit a small place called Port St. Mary, a really nice day out. Another day we walked from one end of the beach to the other, stopping for chips to eat on the beach with a small bottle of lemonade.

On the beach we talked about putting a letter in the lemonade bottle then throwing it out to sea. We talked about the people who would find the bottle then send a message back to us. Our Gordon stopped the conversation by saying, "You stupid lot, you haven't got any paper or a pen."

What he said brought us all back to reality, he was right, but it's nice to dream now and again of the people in far off places, and their land and one of the bottles could have gone all the way home, someone standing at the landing stage looking out across the Mersey might just see the bottle.

"Joyce you are stupid, I've just said you have no pen or paper."

Thinking about the Mersey and talking about it started to make me feel very home-sick, my chin had dropped on my chest. I wanted to go home.

"Who wants an ice-cream? Come on, speak up."

It was one of the woman who had taken us along the beach for a walk. Me! Me! Me! All the kids wanted one including myself. I was okay after that. The food was good, the weather was good, the holiday was good. We were given six pence a day to spend on whatever we wanted, sweets, ice-cream, the works.

Three of us shared a bedroom, I slept with one of the girls in a double bed while the other lucky girl had her own bed. We had the time of our lives, but one night I was woken by the sound of Mrs Brown's voice. She was dragging me out of bed shouting, "Still wetting the bed I see, we'll cure you!"

Dragging me into the bathroom, she filled the bath full of cold water and put me in it for what seemed like hours. I think she forgot about me, until the lady of the house came into me saying, "Come on love, let's get you out."

The lady helped me get into my warm dry pyjamas. "Sorry love, you'll have to sleep there," she said, pointing to a mattress on the floor.

I slept on that mattress for the rest of the holiday. I never did wet the bed again. The cold water bath must have worked, but the girl whose bed I'd shared did wet the bed, so I never did find out if it was her or me.

On the beach we were having a sandcastle competition to be held at the end of the week. The prize was three shillings to the winner. I made the best sandcastle with a moat around it, it looked lovely. I even spent a penny on a flag to put on the top. I'd worked on it all day, then it was time for the judges to walk round each one to mark up. I stood there alongside my pride and joy, I didn't get the three shillings, so all that day was wasted, I could have done other things and I'd spent a penny on a stupid flag.

The holiday was over, my very first holiday and it flew over, but it was great and I loved it.

Back at the Cottage, Mrs Brown had found someone else to have a go at so started to leave me alone. A lot of the kids had visitors on a Sunday afternoon and would have oranges, sweets and crisps to share with the rest of us, who had no-one to come. Mrs Brown always played the part as a nice person, but as soon as the visitors had gone, she would turn right back to the horrible fat woman she was. I'd look at her and promise that one day I'd get her back for all the cruel things she did, not only to me, but to all the rest that came after me.

8

Soon we were back home with Nan again, never to go back and trying to get on with our lives and settling down to a proper home life.

Me and Ruby didn't play with the tar again, we were older now and boys were more interesting. I was growing up to be a right 'tom boy'. I was always with the lads, we used to climb walls, play kick the can, sometimes make holes in a can and then put a string handle on it and then light a fire inside the can and swing it around our head or play ollies in the gutter, the big ollie was called a 'bollywasher' and was worth three small ones if you hit it. The lads were good at playing ollies and always tried to hit our bollywashers, "Give us a kiss and we'll give you the bollywasher back," John would say.

"Get lost, I'd sooner kiss our dog."

"Do you and Ruby fancy going to Newsham Park to go on the rowing boats?" John would ask.

"Yeah, okay, who's going?"

"Well, me, Dave, Billy and Ronny. What do you think?"

"Yeah, if my Nan will give me a tanner."

"If she won't, you go and wait the other side of the boating lake, and we'll pick you up."

"It's not worth asking then, why pay a tanner if you can do that?"

"Christ, Joyce, anything for nothing!"

"Well, why not?"

"Come on, then, all the others are waiting for us."

"What about Billy, where is he?"

"Ronny and Dave said he's in Letterstone Street."

"Come on, Billy, are you going or what?"

"Yeah, hang on, wait till I tell my Ma."

On the way to Newsham Park we passed Margaret Street Baths.

"Anyone fancy the baths instead?" I asked.

"Don't be stupid, none of us have got a cossy."

"We can go back and get them."

I was out voted on that one. Just as well, I didn't have any money. We stayed all day at the Park. We went on the boats and played football – I had my legs kicked from under me and my blouse got ripped, it still looked better than John's shirt. He didn't have a button left, but his Mam was great about it, after we told her what had happened. The story was made up, but she believed it. We told her lads had jumped us and John's shirt got ripped. Well, he shouldn't try to rip my blouse.

On Saturday afternoon, we would walk into town to the back of the market, to look for any wooden boxes left there by the fruit and fish men. We'd then try to break the boxes by putting them against the wall or gutter and giving it a slam with our feet. After we had quite a bit would stack it all into a bigger box we had put to one side, or our Gordon and Jeanette would break the wood, and I'd have to go to find a big box to drag the wood home.

Once home, we would start to put the wood into bundles, tie off with string or left over knitting wool, then sell around the doors for tuppence, just so we could go to the pictures on Saturday afternoon. In the winter it would be easy and fun to earn a few bob by clearing the snow from peoples steps and path, that always got our picture money.

First we would go to Ernie's Cafe on the corner of Breck Road and Everton Road for a bowl of soup and piece of dry bread, or a hot Vimto, then off to the pictures to whatever was showing that week. Now, if it was a cowboy film, all the kids left the pictures with their coat over their shoulders with just the top button fastened, if you had one. Then they'd run down Breck Road or wherever they lived smacking their bums like they were riding a horse.

At one time most films where about Davy Crockett, who wore a fur hat with a tail at the back. All the lads started to wear these hats just so they looked like him. Not a very good time for the local cats as lots started to go missing.

Mrs Davies who lived next door to us had a baby every year, or that's what I thought, as the house was full of kids, aged from eleven right down to two, with not a year between them. Each baby had their own second-hand pram, because by the time the baby was too big for the pram, the other kids would have wrecked it.

Most kids in the street would wait for the right time, then ask for the old pram, so they could use the wheels for a go-kart by putting a wooden box on top of the chassis. We would be made up if our Gordon got the wheels, as we could use it to bring the wood home from town, instead of trying to drag it.

All the kids wanted to see the new baby Mrs Davies had just had. We would take it in turn to go up the stairs to her bedroom, and there at the side of her bed in the bottom drawer of her dressing table, would be a lovely new baby. I don't think she ever got much rest, as all her other kids would be running riot downstairs, but she never shouted at the kids, and although they seemed poor to us, the kids were always happy.

Having so many kids must have taken its toll as she was very thin and drawn, yet they always found time to laugh at one thing or another. I can still remember her making a big pan of scouse, then taking the meat out for her husband – so the kids had what she would call blind scouse. She lived from hand to mouth, yet it was a very happy family. It was a routine to hear Mrs Davies bang on the joining wall with a poker. Nan would say, "Go out the back and see what Mrs Davies wants."

We would often pass sugar or a cup of milk over the wall if she had run out or vice-versa. We used the back wall so the nosy neighbours couldn't see what was going on.

People say 'new baby new house', and that's what happened to Mrs. Davies. There were eight kids in a two bedroom house that was far too small now for the family. One day they were there as normal, and the next they had moved right out of the neighbourhood to the outskirts of Liverpool.

My Nan was becoming very strict with me and I had to be in by seven o'clock or I'd get a good telling off or should I say 'screaming off'.

"You will bring nothing but no good to this house. Always with the lads, just let me catch you, you'll get the rounds of the kitchen."

The more she shouted, the more I stayed with the lads. They were my mates, we never did anything wrong. There must of been about eight of us, and we always stayed together; when one went home we all did. We would play rounders or kick the can at the bottom of Hodson Place or Letterstone Street or sometimes go and play up by the waterworks.

On the top of the waterworks was a bowling

green and we would watch the men playing bowls, and more times than not, annoy the Park Keeper. He would chase us all down the steps if we gave him cheek.

I would always have to be home by seven o'clock, especially on a Friday or Saturday night, as Nan wanted us all in, so she could go out on the town. Our Jeanette would try to get us to go to bed, but as all kids we would play her up. Our Gordon and me would make paper airplanes then throw them out the bedroom window for all the kids in the street. The kids would be screaming and shouting for more, then we would hear our Jeanette run up the stairs to see what we were up to.

"What the hell is going on?" she would demand.

By this time, our Gordon and me had dived back into bed trying to look all innocent, only all the paper on the bedroom floor gave the game away.

"Just wait till my Nan comes in, she'll belt the pair of you. Now get to sleep."

We would hear the front door open and Jeanette telling the kids to get away from the front door.

"Now clear off the lot of you!"

By this time we were back up against the window, looking down at all the kids getting told off. As soon as we heard the door slam, we'd dive back into bed. Jeanette would try and creep upstairs to catch us, but the third stair used to creak so we knew what she was up to. This would go on for hours, then we would hear Nan's high heel shoes coming down the street, and as she put the key in the door, we would hear a man's voice, never the same voice, each time a different one. Some would leave after a couple of hours, some the next day. Nan always said, "Don't get up yet. I'll call you."

That always meant she had a man with her. She always had money that day as she would give me tuppence for sweets.

It was years later that I realised what she was up to. At the time I didn't know. I was far too young.

If she came home alone it meant no money and Nan in a bad temper. After a few months she started to bring home the same man. He was tall and very stockily built, his name was Bob Hardie and he moved into our home. I don't know when he moved in, he was just there all the time and as strict as Nan.

He kept a trumpet in Nan's bedroom. I'd look at it when they were out. One night I was looking at the trumpet and tried to play it and didn't hear Bob Hardie come in. He went berserk, dragging me by the hair across the bedroom, "You keep your bloody hands off! Don't let me ever catch you again, do you hear me? I'll break your bloody legs if I catch you again!"

It was no use telling Nan about him, it would only cause a row, but it never ended there, they would have big fights and Nan would get thrown across the kitchen by him. If Jeanette or one of us started to scream, "You leave my Nan alone!" we would come off worse. He would try to slap us, but the three of us would run out the back or upstairs to get out of his way. He always smelt of beer.

Time after time when Nan and Bob Hardie went out on the town, the return was always the same. A big fight would start and go on for hours. We would be under the bed clothes listening, too frightened to move. The house was so unhappy. Our Jeanette would always say, "I wish Nan would get rid of him, I hate him."

When we got Nan alone we would ask her to get rid of him, but it always fell on deaf ears.

Time after time I'd get to the front door only to hear Nan and Bob shouting at each other, and I'd turn and walk away, back down the street, to all the lads standing on the corner.

"What's up with you, thought you were goin' home?"

"What for? To listen to them two?"

"Want to go to Dave's house? His ma's out."

"Why not, Nan won't miss me. Anyway I don't care."

I was starting to change, and I didn't like myself very much. The longer I stayed out the more Nan or Bob would shout at me. I didn't want to go home. When I was told to stay in for the week, I would be out the back door and into the next street, or I'd go to Ruby's back yard to play.

Ruby's Nan would come out to go to the lav and say, "Your Nan's been out in the street shouting you."

I'd just shrug my shoulders. "So?"

"Never mind 'so', you get yourself home."

"Come on, Ruby let's go."

"She's not going anywhere, you get yourself off," she would shout from the lav.

The two of us would whisper, "I'll say ta-ra, and you go in, I'll see you at the bottom of Hodson Place, okay? In ten minutes. don't forget."

"See you tomorrow Ruby, ta-ra."

"Yeah, see you Joyce."

"See you Mrs Appleton."

Ruby would close the back gate then go in, wait for her Nan to get off the lav, then go back out to meet me at the bottom of her entry and Hodson Place.

"How come your Nan lets you play out?"

"I don't know. You better watch out, your Nan's at the door. She's just asked me if I'd seen you."

"What did you say?"

"No, of course."

"Shall we go to Everton Brow?"

"What for? There's nothing there."

"I can't hang around here."

"Where's the lads? I haven't seen them all day."

"John said they where going to Kirkby to get some apples by Spinny Woods."

"Shall we go?"

"Get lost, they'll be on their way home now. Anyway, I've got no money."

"Joyce, you never have any money."

"I know, it's not my fault."

"Ruby! Quick! There's the Hardie fella going the pub, stand in front of me quick!"

"He's gone, didn't know he drank in there."

"Doesn't, bet that's 'cos I'm not in."

"You'd better go home."

"Ruby, shut up, I'll go when I'm ready."

"So you haven't seen Joyce eh?"

A voice behind us made us jump.

"I've just seen her now."

Nan must have been standing there for ages.

"You've just been talking about going for apples."

"No, that was yesterday."

"You little liar! And you get in now. I've been

shouting you for ages, you're in for the week," giving
me a belt over the back of my head.

"Get yourself up those stairs now."

"Get yourself up those stairs now, that's all you
say."

"Don't you answer me back, you cheeky little
bugger," she smacked me, "that will teach you."

I jumped to the top end of the bed so Nan's arm
would not reach me, to stop her getting another slap
in. It didn't work, slap, slap.

"That will teach you to come in when I shout
you, and you stay away from that one across the
road."

"I hate you, I hate you."

The tears ran down my face, but I didn't make a
sound. I was more interested in looking at the red
mark at the top of my leg where I knocked it on the
end of the bed. That had hurt me more than Nan's
slap. When I get some money, I thought, I'm going
to run away from here. I got undressed for bed,
banging my shoes on the floor with temper, and
dumping my clothes on the floor at the bottom of
the bed.

I came home one afternoon and there on the mantle piece was two shillings, one on each end. I took the money and went out.

The first place was the sweet shop. The two shillings bought me a lot of sweets. I'd never had so many and had to stay out the rest of the day to eat them or Nan would ask where I'd got the money from. When I got back home and walked into the kitchen, Nan was shouting, "Who's taken the money? Have you got the money?"

"No."

Well, I didn't have it, I'd spent it, but she didn't know that.

"You little liar. Gordon has been out all day, he didn't take it. Jeanette has been with me, she didn't take it. That leaves you!"

Bob had already started to take off his leather belt and grabbing me by the shoulder dragged me upstairs. I lost count through the screams how many times he used his belt, but my bum and back were stinging like hell.

He left the room saying, "That's the last time you steal any money from this house."

I could have told him that. I cried myself to sleep after hearing my Nan shout upstairs, "And you get no tea tonight, you can go without."

The bedroom was dark when I woke up to Bob Hardie standing over me. He put his hand on my arm, "How are you?"

He leaned over me to give me a cuddle to calm me down and his hands were all over me. I knew what he was doing was wrong, it was all wrong. Why was he trying to take my bed clothes off?

"Move your hand, you're hurting me."

Where's my Nan? I wondered. What's he doing? His breath smelt of beer, he was trying to talk in my ear, but I couldn't hear what he was saying with his face up against the pillow.

"Get off me, you're hurting me."

This man was so big and heavy on top of me, he was trying to put his hand up my nightie to move my legs. The weight of his body stopped me from moving away. I could feel something hard go up inside me. The pain! Oh, what was he doing to me? He was pushing up and down, and putting my hands under his chest to push him off only made him go faster.

"I want my Nan, leave me alone, I want my Nan."

"It's okay, don't worry, you're all right."

Wiping my nose and tears on my bed sheet he moved away.

"Now, don't say anything to your Nan or anyone else okay. Tomorrow I'll get you some sweets. Your Nan will smack you if you say anything."

He left the room and closed the door. I was scared to look. I knew I was bleeding, I could feel it. The tears were burning into my face and my eyes were stinging. I sat up to look under the sheet, but there was no blood, it was just sticky. I wiped myself on the tangled sheet, and buried my face in my pillow until sleep took over.

As the days passed, I stopped going out to play. I didn't want to eat. This man had frightened me. I wanted to tell Nan, but what? How did I tell her what I didn't know? Just how did I explain? Would they fight again, would she scream at me?

If Nan went on a message, I always tried to go with her or play out until she came home. There was no way I'd stay in the house alone, just in case the Hardie fella was there. If Jeanette or Gordon was in, then I felt safe. If he asked me to do anything, I'd just stare at him, but would never do what he wanted. Nan would say, "He's talking to you, why don't you answer?"

I'd shrug my shoulders and tut, then look over at him, "Do it yourself."

More than once he tried to give me a belt. I'd look up at him, screw my eyes up and shout, "Just you try, I'll tell my Nan and our Jeanette on you."

"Ya cheeky little bitch!"

"Get out of our house, we hate you, we all hate you!" I shouted.

"Who the hell are you talking to?"

"You, go on get out, and leave us alone."

He made a move to hit me, but I was out the back door and down the entry.

I started to hate my Mam for leaving us. If she was still here then this would never of happened, but she wasn't here, she was dead. I wanted to be dead as well, it would be all my fault if Nan had another big row and threw Bob Hardie out of the house. I wanted to run away, just to get away from this man, but I didn't have to run away as he left one afternoon, taking the gas and electric meter money with him.

I told Nan later on what had gone on. I don't think she really believed me. If she did, she never did say much. I'm not sure what I wanted, but I didn't get it. I loved my Nan and I wanted her love, but she didn't show it and over the years to come, my feelings for her left me. Nan had let me down when I wanted her most and I never forgot.

★ ★ ★ ★ ★

The months passed into years, Nan had stopped going out now, but was just as strict with me. I was still hanging round with lads, they were my mates. Nan could never understand that, she always said I'd come to no good.

I was half an hour late coming home one night and Nan gave me round the kitchen, calling me fit to burn and saying that tomorrow I was going over the doctors. I felt her hand across my face so hard I fell against the stairs. The next day she had me out of bed early so as to go with her to the doctors for him to examine me. The only man who had touched me was one of her lovers and I told her that. The first, but not the last. I stood my ground.

Nan didn't take me the doctors, but backed down. That must have been the last straw for me because that week I made a visit to our adoption officer. Her name was Miss Murphy, a big woman who used to wear men's shoes and always wore old fashioned suits. The cigarettes she smoked were held half way down her fingers. I never told her or anyone about Bob Hardie, but did tell her that I was very unhappy at home and wanted to leave.

She came to our house and spoke to Nan. I waited about a week when Miss Murphy came to tell me that she had found a family in town. The family were looking forward to having me. All I knew was that they had two children, not far off the same age as me and I was to leave the following Thursday night after school. Miss Murphy was to pick me up and take me to meet the new family. Yes, I was looking forward to getting away from what I thought a loveless home.

On the Thursday night, I had gone upstairs right from school to put my things into a bag – my clothes, shoes and all the little things that was special to me, then I waited and waited. An hour or so had gone by before Nan came upstairs and said she had been down to see Miss Murphy that afternoon and told her that I had changed my mind. How could she do this to me? How could Miss Murphy just take her word without even asking me?

I lost faith in Miss Murphy after that and never wanted to see her again. Yes, all grown ups are all the same, they all let you down. Each time Miss Murphy came up to see us I was out the back door and up the entry to play in the next street, or if it was raining, sit on the lav in the back yard. The two people I thought I could trust had let me down and it took me years before the trust ever came back.

11

It was 1957 and I was 12. Jeanette and our Gordon
had started work and had a few bob in their pockets,
so they could afford to go out and enjoy themselves.

They would ask me to go to the shops for this
and that, but I would only go it they would give me
tuppence or if it was a shop right down Breck Road,
I'd ask for sixpence to go. I'd pull every stunt in the
book to get a few pence off our Gordon 'cos he was
so mean and still is. He never knew about the times
I'd already took my tuppence then still try for more
for going the shops for him. The times he did catch
me out, he would batter me and Nan would try to
get between us to stop the fight.

Now our Gordon could go for a drink on
Saturday night, fall in the door at quarter to eleven,

drop his money all over the floor and tell you next day he was down a penny. I used to love setting our Gordon up, although things were hard we had our laughs.

Being older, he had to move out of our bedroom and into the back room. As you walked into his room the bed was on the left, on the right was a dressing table, at the bottom of his bed was an alcove that had a curtain across, behind the curtain was a rail going from wall to wall to hang his clothes on. The rail was a hand rail off the trams that a fella down the street who had worked on the trams had got for us. I think Nan gave half a crown for it as it was stainless steel and looked nice and posh, even behind the curtain.

At night Nan would come upstairs and tell us a story. We always asked for a good one. Now, one night the story was in full swing and to make it sound really good Nan used to put her foot out of the bed and knock those horrible handles on the chest of drawers. Our Gordon would shout in, "Nan, what's that noise?"

We would be laughing under the sheets trying not to let our Gordon hear us. The knock, knock, knock would put the wind of God up our Gordon.

One night Nan was telling us a story about the headless horseman, driving along the dark road, when I crept out of my bed and into our Gordon's bedroom on my hands and knees. As I was passing his bed, I could see Gordon looking up at the ceiling with his hands underneath his head. Very quietly I'd got to the bottom of the bed, the idea was to try and get behind the curtain, then just walk out at the right time to shake the curtain to frighten our Gordon.

The story got really creepy and the thought of those handles that Nan was giving the 'Bells of Shannon' had started to frighten me, so I just stood up. Our Gordon screamed and fell out of the bed – that really frightened me, his screaming so loud. The both of us tried to get through the bedroom door at the same time. That night we all lost sleep, and we still talked about that night years later.

Another day, our Gordon fell in Newsham Park Lake head first and he had to walk home soaking wet and cold. I'd told him that Nan had been looking for him all day and if I'd seen him to tell him he had to go to bed as punishment with no tea. Nan came in from the shops and asked where our Gordon was. I told her that our Gordon felt tired and wanted no tea, he just wanted to go to bed. Nan thought he might be coming down with something, possibly a cold. I just laughed, she could be right.

Another time, our Gordon had gone out on his

bike for the day with the Bike Club he was in. Nan had done the tea. Jeanette, Nan and myself had all eaten and what was left on our plates we scraped off onto a plate for the dog. Our Gordon's tea was in the oven. When he came home Nan told him his tea was in the back, but I'd washed the dishes and mopped the kitchen floor, picking up the dogs plate and putting it in the oven until the floor had dried.

When our Gordon had finished his tea, I washed the rest of the dishes, then onto the cooker with a quick wipe over, only to find Gordon's dinner in the oven. Gordon had eaten the dogs dinner. Later he said his dinner was nice, but wondered why Nan had mashed it all up.

"Gordon, if you liked your dinner that much, there's another one in the oven if you want it."

I had great pleasure telling all the kids in our street that our Gordon had eaten the dogs dinner. I soon stopped as I felt his hand across the back of my head.

"I'll get you back for that you, just you wait."

Our Gordon used to leave his bike in the back yard, when he was out I'd let the tyre down, then I'd see him blowing it up again. As soon as his back was turned I'd be out again letting it down. He would have the bike in bits all over the yard cleaning it, or putting air here or there. If I went down the lav, I'd pinch a bit of his bike and hide it, maybe a screw or his spanner, he used to go mad, screaming, "Who's got my spanner?"

"What you looking at me for, I've not got it."

"Nan, our Gordon is swearing at me."

"What the hell is goin' on out here?"

"It's her, she's pinched my spanner!"

"No I haven't, I haven't seen your stupid spanner."

"I'm warning you Joyce, if you've got his spanner, give it him back."

"Here's your stupid spanner, spoil sport."

"I told you she had it, you leave my things alone," he grabbed me by the shoulder and added, "or I'll kill you."

"Oh, will you now, just try."

"That's it! You get in, and you put that bike back together. Any more fightin, I'll sell the bloody bike."

"Ya won't, I paid for that bike meself."

"What? You spend money? Have you heard that Nan, our Gordon spend money!"

"Leave him alone, come in."

"Ah, leave him alone, my little baby, are you Nan's little blue eye?"

"Nan, tell her or I'll kill her."

"Who's turn is it to wash up?" Nan said looking at me.

"It's our Gordon's."

"No, it's not. I did it last night."

"You always say that, you didn't do them last night, I did. We had scouse and the bottom of the pan was burnt. I had to leave it in soak."

"Joyce, you didn't, that was the night before. I did them last night, Gordon it's your turn." Nan said walking into the kitchen.

"Oh, Nan, I'm goin' out tonight, I haven't got time."

"You'll have to make time then, won't you Gordon?"

"I'll do them for you, but it will cost you."

"How much?"

"A shilling."

"What? Forget it, I'll do them meself."

"Ya tight-fisted get, just you wait till you want a message, you do it yourself."

"I will."

"You'll soon pay a shillling when you see the dishes, there's loads, Nan's made steam puddin, there's three pans, and loads of dishes. Ha, what time did you say you where goin out?"

"I'll give ya a tanner then."

"No."

"Oh, go on, a tanner."

"Will you two shut up. I've had this all day, now

pack it in the two of you. Gordon, do the bloody dishes yourself, but don't use the water in the kettle yet, till I've made a pot of tea."

"Oh eh, Nan, I could have got a tanner off him."

"I'll bloody tanner ya."

When we were young, Nan always said never pick up a comb in the street, it belongs to the banshee, she howls at night as she combs her hair and her hair is all tatty, so that's why you see combs in the street with no teeth, the banshee has used it. I always think of that banshee when I see a comb in the street, but our Gordon took it more to heart as it put the wind of God up him.

Now Jeanette was the complete opposite, a very sensible girl, who unlike me, spoke nice, she was slim with fair hair and got on well with everyone to the point were Nan was always on my back,

"Why can't you talk like Jeanette? Why can't you dress like Jeanette?"

I was fed up with hearing about our Jeanette and why wasn't I like her. Yes, I was fed up to the back teeth and often made it known. You are what you are, no one can change you. You have to be yourself no matter what. What Nan didn't realise was that our Jeanette was working and could afford to buy nice clothes.

I was still as school. I didn't have any money, no

way I could buy shoes, gloves and handbag to match, well not for a lousy sixpence anyway, and I'd only get an extra sixpence for doing Jeanette or Gordon's dishes if they were going out, or run the length of Breck Road on a message. So how could I dress like our Jeanette?

"You should stay in more. Never mind hanging round corners with the lads, you'll come to no good. You'll bring shame to this house, no one else, only you."

Yes, I'd heard those words so many times before. It was like an old record being played over and over again, but never to Jeanette, not goody-two-shoes. Jeanette never did wrong in Nan's eyes, little miss prim and proper.

Well, it's a funny old world how things turn out. It wasn't that long after Nan had had a go at me, when our Jeanette asked me to go up Breck Road with her. Now that's something we had long stopped doing together. She wanted to tell me she was pregnant and didn't know how to tell Nan.

"What? You're having a baby?"

"I think so."

"How do you know?"

"Oh, for God's sake, Joyce! I just know!"

Jeanette had been courting Tommy for about three years. He had done his stint in the Army and had got posted to Singapore for about eighteen months. His homecoming must have been a good one. I didn't believe it, goody-two-shoes was having a baby!

I left our Jeanette and made my way home. This was one bit of news I had to tell.

Nan was sitting by the fire reading the paper when I walked in. I sat down in the chair opposite.

"There's tea in the pot, I've just made it."

"No, you're okay, I don't want one."

"Thought you were going the shops with Jeanette."

"Oh, yeah I was. Nan, you know you've said for years you wanted me to be like Jeanette?"

"Well?"

Nan put the paper down and looked across at me.

"What the hell are you going on about?"

"I'll tell you what the hell I'm going on about. Your precious Jeanette has just told me up Breck Road that's she's pregnant."

"You what?"

Yes, I'd waited years for this moment. I could have knocked Nan down with a feather. It gave me great pleasure looking at Nan's face. She didn't blink, just stared at me, then picked up the poker and started to poke the fire.

"Yeah, it's a funny old world, all these years you've said 'why don't you act like Jeanette, or look like her'. Do you want me to get pregnant? I don't think so."

Before she could answer, our Jeanette walked in the back way.

"Don't bother to tell her, I've done it for you."

"You sly little bitch."

All hell broke out. Nan started to shout, not at our Jeanette, but me. Our Jeanette, still standing by the kitchen door, was also shouting about me going over her head telling Nan. I jumped up out of the chair and made towards Jeanette. I grabbed her hair and we ended up having one hell of a fight. I'd started to take all my anger out on her, and Nan pulled me off shouting, "Leave her alone! Leave her alone! She's pregnant!"

"Take your hands off me, I could lose the baby."

"I don't give a shit!"

Walking out the room, I made my way upstairs. Slamming the bedroom door, I sat on the bed. Christ, I thought, she's pregnant and I come off worse. I stayed there for ages just feeling sorry for myself and having a sulk.

"Joyce, if you want any tea, you'd better come down or it goes in the bin."

Oh, if that was Jeanette it would be, "er, love, do

you want it on a tray?"

Oh no, not me, mine goes in the bin. When I came downstairs, Tommy, our Jeanette's fella was there. Our Jeanette must have told him everything and about the fight. He just stood behind me and leaned over the back of my chair saying, "You want to grow up, you're still shittin yellow shit."

"Who the hell are you talking to?"

"I'm talking to you, don't ever play that stunt again, do you hear me?"

"Oh shut up, who are you to tell me?"

"You keep your hands to yourself in future, she's having my baby. Now I'm warning you, okay?"

"And who's fault is it she's pregnant? Not mine!"

"I've told you, grow up!"

Jeanette and me hardly spoke to each other after that, and Nan was very cool with me.

I'd made it plain to everyone I wasn't going to the wedding. Our Jeanette had tried to talk me round, but I wasn't having any.

She asked me to go with her for her wedding outfit, only to be told to get lost. I just did my best to stay out of it. Our Gordon had a new suit, Nan was all rigged out with a nice new suit and hat. Jeanette also looked really nice. On the morning of her wedding, she again asked me to go

"Will you please come to my wedding? Look, let

bygones be bygones, I've only got one sister, Gordon is going, come on love, come to my wedding."

"Go to hell!"

"Right, that's it. I'm not upsetting myself today. I've asked you, I can't do no more."

"Then just shut up and leave me alone."

I was told by friends that I'd missed a really good day and the do at night was great. They had a live band and lots of food.

"Well, there would be."

"Joyce, you're stupid, why didn't you go?"

"Look Ruby, I didn't want to go, now leave it alone."

"Have you been to see her new flat?"

"No, have you?"

"No."

"Then shut up then."

"Joyce, what's to do with you lately? You're always biting my head off."

"I'm sick to death hearing about our Jeanette, okay?"

Nan had put a wedge between us without knowing it and that wedge lasted for years to come, through no fault of our own. I had started to hate my sister and all she stood for and I always did the complete opposite to her. *I'll show the lot of them* when I leave school, I thought, *I'll show them just what I really am, yes, I'm better than the lot of them and I'll prove it one day.*

12

Eighteen months later and it was my turn to leave school. I had spent the last four years at Steers Street school, situated off Everton Road. It was an all girls school, although some of the hard girls were built like fella's. Rub them up the wrong way and God help you.

Now I could hold my own, but I had to think twice with some of these. I sort of took a step back, didn't fancy my nose splattered over my face, not in my last year anyway. Most of the teachers just bored me to tears – I mean, take the maths teacher, all I wanted to do was look out of the window, until I felt the ruler slam on the desk.

"If you don't take any notice, you'll never get anywhere in life."

Now she never said a truer word. I ended up in a factory. I'd had an interview at Ogdens Tobacco Company and was to start work a week later. At the interview I had to have my school report and birth certificate, so I had to go to Brougham Terrace to get the birth certificate.

There were about five people already waiting including a couple giving details to get married, the fella was a nice looking man. The girl he wanted to marry looked like she'd been hit with a cricket bat, an ugly woman with no pride in her clothes. On her feet she had plastic flip-flops and her feet were as black as the ace of spades underneath and had hard skin around the edge of her heel. Her skirt told everyone in the queue she had a dog or cat that was molting, and she had lanky greasy hair. I know love is blind, but this fella must be stupid as well.

Two men at the other window were there to register the birth of a baby. I could hear them talking about going out that night to wet the babies head.

An old man was sitting next to me on the bench, who stunk to high heaven. I've never smelt anything like it before, and when he spoke to me, he only had three teeth and they were brown.

The couple who wanted to get married stood back to let me or the old man go up to the window.

"Go on, girl, you go, I'm being seen to."

"Ta."

Was I glad to move!

The lady came to the desk and asked my date of birth.

"12th July 1945," I replied.

A quarter of an hour later the lady came back.

"Sorry love, but that's not your date of birth, it's the tenth not the twelfth."

I've never felt so stupid, standing there with people behind me who could hear every word being said.

"Er, girl, you can be like the queen, two birthdays!"

The old man thought it was funny. At least someone was happy. I wasn't and the ugly woman gave her fella a nudge in the rib and started to snigger at me. I could hear her saying to her fella, "The age of her, fancy not knowing your own birthday."

"Ha, love, that's the difference between you and me. I can change my birthday, you'll always look like that."

"What d'ya mean?"

"What I said, I can change my birthday from the twelfth to the tenth, you will always be ugly."

"It takes one to know one."

"You said it, girl."

I'd gone right through my fifteen years with the wrong birthday. How could Nan make such a big mistake? My God, couldn't she even get that right? I walked back down those steps feeling so unloved and unhappy. No one knew my right birthday, I didn't believe it.

*   *   *   *   *

At the beginning of August 1960, I was off to my first job at Ogdens Tobacco Company off West Derby Road. My job was to strip the tobacco off the stem, hence the job title 'a stripper' in the 21 leaf room. A job I'd been looking forward to for the past year. The last year of school had been a killer for me. I never thought the time would come when those big school gates shut on me for the last time, not that being at Steers Street school had really taught me anything. They had just tried to pick up the pieces from all the other school's I'd gone to over the years.

However, a prefect badge and the fact that I had not a bad school report under my belt must have made some impression on Ogdens, as they took me on.

Those days, to work in that factory, you needed a

letter from our Lord or had a member of your family already working there. Our Lord didn't help, but our Jeanette did as she had gone there herself right from school so that opened the door for me.

The day of the interview, I was up at the crack of dawn to make sure all my papers I needed were still in the brown envelope and all my clean clothes were pressed and over the back of the chair. Nan had been up early and cooked me a nice breakfast, toast, boiled egg and a cup of tea.

"Now, don't forget to use your manners," she reminded me.

"I know, Nan."

"Those people notice all these things, you remember that."

"Don't worry, Nan, I'll be okay."

"Now if they say, do you have any questions to ask, mention the wages."

"Nan, I don't have to, this letter says all that."

"Well, don't just sit there looking stupid."

"Oh Nan, give it a rest, Christ! Look at the time! I've got to be there for half nine."

"Who else is going, anyone you know?"

"Yeah, Bunny."

"Oh, at least you're not on your own."

"Bunny's Dad is going with her."

"Ya don't want me there do you?"

"No, you're all right."

I pushed my plate away. "Nan, just pass us my coat. What do you think, will I pass?"

"Yeah, you look nice, turn round let's see the back."

"See ya, Nan, I should be back by eleven."

"Good luck, I'll keep my fingers crossed."

You could smell Ogdens streets away, and the smell of tobacco got stronger as I walked into Boundry Lane, the main office where the interview was to take place.

"All right, Bunny. Hello, Mr Bunn."

"Hiya, Joyce, my nerves have gone."

"I know how you feel, I didn't sleep last night."

"Hope we get the job, Bun."

"Yeah, it will be great if we end up working together."

"What time is your interview, Bun?"

"Er, hang on. Dad, let's see that letter again."

"Oh, eh Bun, that's a good start, don't you know what time you should be here? Could be this afternoon."

"Oh, behave!"

"What time is yours, Joyce?"

"Half nine, Mr Bunn."

"Miss Miller, would you like to come through please."

"Here goes!"

"Best of luck, Joyce."

"Thanks, Bunny."

I walked along the corridor past one door that was open. Inside I could see girls sitting at desks typing, papers stacked high. I didn't fancy that job, it would be like going back to school. No chance anyway with my brain, can't even spell.

"Good morning, Miss Miller, how are you?"

"Good morning, fine, thank you," remembering what Nan had said about manners.

"Sit down please."

"Thank you." I was doing okay, Nan would be proud.

"Do you have your school report and the other papers you were asked to bring?"

"Yes," I replied, handing the lady the envelope.

"Going by your school report, you did quite well."

Christ! Had I picked our Jeanette's up by mistake? I didn't think I had.

"You made prefect, very good."

"Thank you."

"And your date of birth is 10th July 1945, is that right?"

"Yes, that's right?"

This time I'd got it right, my real birthday.

"Well, all your papers seem to be in order."

Miss Johnson handed me back the brown envelope, as she told me all about the job I was to do, and the room I'd be working in. It wasn't the same as our Jeanette's, but she told me I'd see her on breaks and at dinner time. I'd got the job, it would be confirmed by post.

Outside I sat on the wall and waited for Bunny and her Dad, hoping she also did well at the interview. I'd met Bunny twelve months ago, her older sister and our Jeanette where good friends, and we just hit it off. We ended up the best of mates.

"If I ever get married, Bunny, I want you to be my bridesmaid."

"Well, you can be mine."

"I wonder who gets married first?"

"Joyce, it will definitely be you."

"Go way! What makes you say that?"

"Just a guess, that's all."

"Well, he's got to be tall, blonde and blue eyes. What about you Bunny?"

"Oh, dark, handsome with a few bob – ha!"

"Hiya, Bunny, how did it go? I hope you got the job."

"Yeah, but they're going to let me know by letter."

"Oh, that's great Bun, what room are you in? She

told me twenty one leaf."

"Oh Joyce! I'm made up, mine's the same."

"Right, I'll have to get off and tell my Nan, see you soon okay? See ya, Mr. Bunn."

"Tara, Joyce."

The walk home made me think of all the money I would be getting. Now I'd have a job, all the nice clothes I could buy, make-up, the lot. Maybe I could put a few bob away. Just think, now I didn't have to pinch the sterry bottles off steps just to buy a loosy and one match, now I could buy my first packet of five cigarettes.

The times the teacher had seen my finger brown with the ciggy, she would hold my finger up to the class and shout, "What's this?"

"Don't know, Miss."

I tried to rub my finger on the wall on the way to school to get rid of the nicotine stain, and I never wanted my Nan to see it, she would just crack up if she knew I smoked. Our Jeanette knew, or I think she did, but she never said anything, and our Gordon definitely knew. He would see the smoke coming out the lav door, but he never seemed to bother, maybe he was smoking as well, although I never caught him at it.

The starting pay was three pounds, thirteen shillings a week. In those days it was classed as a good wage and once a year you got a bonus. At eighteen you were given a packet of forty cigarettes each week, so it wasn't a bad place to work. After a short period of time, when you had the hang of the job, you could go on piece work and earn a lot more money, so the more work I did, the more money I would get.

My first day at work and I was looking forward to starting the new job. No more school uniform or white socks. I was too grown up for them now. I had the world at my feet.

Jeanette had come over to Nan's the night before to tell me she would give me a knock and walk to work with me. She had moved into a house at the top of our street, and only had a month or so before she left Ogdens to have her baby.

"Make sure you put the alarm on. You don't want to oversleep on your first day."

"I know, Nan lent me her clock."

"Okay, I'm off now, see you in the morning. Good night Nan. Good night Joyce. Where's our Gordon?"

"Don't know, I've been to Bunny's."

"I think he went the pictures with his mates." said Nan.

"That's what he's telling you Nan, bet he's been for a pint."

"Maybe."

"Anyway, I've got to go, see ya."

"Nan, I'm off to bed, it's a big day tomorrow."

"Okay, good night Joyce, if I wake up I'll give you a shout."

"Ta, goodnight."

The next morning I was awake before the alarm went off, because I didn't sleep too well. I could smell the toast, so Nan must have been up a while. She met me half way up the stairs.

"I was just coming to give you a call. I've made some toast for you and there's fresh tea in the pot."

"Cheers! Thanks, Nan."

"What time will you be home for dinner?"

"Our Jeanette said it's twelve thirty to one thirty."

"Okay, I'll be here. What do you fancy for your dinner?"

"Whatever."

Nan poured the tea out and put the toast in front of me, "Come on, sit down and get this."

"Yeah, okay Nan, any jam?"

"It's on the shelf in the back. You sit there, I'll get it."

"Oh eh, Nan, you didn't do this for me on my first day," moaned Jeanette, who'd just arrived.

"I did."

Jeanette stood by the kitchen door, looking at Nan find the jam, then pulled up a chair and put her hands on the teapot.

"Room for another cup in there Nan?"

"Yeah, get yourself a cup."

"We'll have to make it quick Joyce, can't be late."

"Listen to her, I'm waiting now."

"See ya Nan."

"Tara."

Walking up Whitefield Road, we could see other girls and fellas making their way to Ogdens and Barker and Dobsons.

"Just think, on the way home tonight, they will smell all nice and we'll stink."

"The things you come out with! Have you got break money?"

"Yeah, Nan gave me two bob?"

"Now don't worry. Your first day will feel strange at first, but you'll get used to it and I'm only in the next room if you need me."

"Oh, I'll be okay, Bunny starts today."

"Well, I'm there if you need me."

"Ta."

The smell of the tobacco inside the factory was a lot stronger than I thought, and all workers had to be in by eight or the doors got shut, leaving you locked out. Girls hanging their coats up made their way to their work rooms, running this way and that way, where to I didn't know.

"Big place this, Jeanette."

"Yeah, now follow me, come on, I'll show you where to go."

We made our way upstairs to the Twenty One Leaf room. Bunny and about eight more new girls were standing talking to a fella in a brown overall, who Jeanette said was the foreman.

"He will show you the ropes. Right, see you at break."

"Tara, see you."

The foreman was a Mr Walker who told us all where to sit. Each in turn sat down, me and Bunny were on the end.

"Okay, girls, you take the tobacco leaf like this, and what you have to do is strip the leaf from the stem, put the leaf in that bag and the stem in the other one. Okay, girls now you have a go."

We all sat in what were called boxes with the tobacco in front and a bag on each side. The leaf went into the right side and the stem into the left, or vice-versa if you where left handed. When that brand of tobacco was finished, the stems were weighed, you had to do a certain amount, then anything over that you got paid for. The quicker you got into the job, the more money you earned.

The new girls got on great and at eleven o'clock 'Music While You Work' was played over the tannoy. The whole room used to sing to the records being played.

"Well, what do you wanna make those eyes at me for, if you don't mean what they say..."

Or we would be singing, "Rambling rose, rambling rose, how I loved you, no one knows..."

Russ Conway was all the go as well, with his Side Saddle. I loved his music and got the last two tickets to see him on the Empire in Lime Street. He started with Roy Orbison. Looking back now it sounds stupid, but the whole of the audience danced in the aisles.

Bunny loved Adam Faith who said, "What do you want if you don't want money?"

We all worked to the music, the quicker the music the faster we worked.

Well, the Friday dinner time came at last on our second week at work and each of us new girls were handed our very first wage packet and it felt great.

Not that I could open it. I had had instructions off Nan that she would do that. Back home I waited for her to finish the egg and chips she had cooked for our dinner.

"Come on Nan, open my wage packet!" I shouted from the kitchen.

"Hang on a minute, do you all want a cup of tea?" Nan shouted back.

"Forget the tea, Christ! Just open the packet!" I shouted back.

At the side of my plate I could see this little brown envelope with small holes so you could check your wages without opening the packet to see if it was all there.

At last Nan picked up the envelope and opened it. "Not bad for your first week's wage" she said, handing me the thirteen shillings. My God, I'd never had so much money and all for myself. I felt great and happy thinking of all the things I could buy and of the nights out with the girls. However, the good feeling didn't last long as me and our Jeanette ended up having a big row over a stupid egg.

Nan had given us a plate of egg and chips and I'd eaten all the chips on my plate. With the egg I'd eaten all the white from around the yolk without breaking it, so all I had on my plate was this big yolk. My next job was to try and take the skin from the top, but oh no, our Jeanette had watched all my hard work and at the last minute stuck a chip in it.

With temper, I threw the plate and the broken yolk up the wall, only to feel Nan's hand on the back of my head. I bounced out of the house and made my way back to work, *stupid cow, goody-two-shoes again,* I thought.

She should have gone to her own house for her dinner, not ours, and this wouldn't have happened. Our Jeanette will have to get used to Tommy working 'lates'. You wouldn't think she was married with a place of her own, she was never away from our house.

No one was allowed to chew or eat sweets or you'd get the sack, but all us new girls had decided to buy each other sweets or a bar of chocolate from our first weeks pay, but we had to hide the sweets under the box inside the foot stool. Mind you we were all taking a chance, putting our jobs on the line, but what the hell. Jobs where ten a penny those days, and we could all act stupid if we got caught. The screams of laughter we did talking about it.

"Right, I'll get ten Mars Bars."

"What are you getting Bunny?"

"Oh, I'll get ten packs of Rolo."

And this is how the conversation went right down

the line.

"She's just said Rolo, don't you get them as well."

"Barbara, stupid, I've just said Mars Bars."

"Bunny, you make a list, then each girl cross off what their gettin, or we'll end up all gettin the bloody same. No wonder we work in a factory – not a brain between us."

"Okay, start thinking of ten sweets."

"Barbara, shut up, that's twice you've said Rolo! For God's sake Bunny, put Rolo down on the list for Barbara! Right, that's your nickname from now on – Rolo!"

"Get lost, Joyce."

The shop was packed with stupid school kids buying a penny toffee and a penny lolliop – should be in school the lot of them.

"Er, excuse me love, can I have ten Mars Bars please?"

"Oi! We were before you!"

"So?"

"Well, we wanna be served as well you know!"

"Dozy, it takes all you lot just to spend twopence."

"I'm with him."

"And I'm with him."

"Okay, lads, those who don't want to be served

outside please."

"Right, love, sorry about that, what was yours?"

"Ten Mars Bars, a packet of five cigs, and a book of matches please."

"Moaning old cow!"

"Cheeky little gets, get to school, go on."

Now I had to get everything upstairs without the foreman seeing them.

"Rolo, where are you putting the sweets?"

"Put them up your sleeve like me, then no one can see them."

"Ha! Let's hope Enid doesn't hide them in her drawers!"

"Joyce! You're terrible saying that!"

"Bunny, pass these along."

"Oh, eh Joyce, keep them down, Mr. Walker's over there."

"Quick, Bunny! Hide them under the leaf."

"My nerves have gone."

"Go on, it's okay, he's gone the other way."

"Look girls, if you go under the box for sweets tell us so we can keep nick for you. Tell you what, Bunny, it's not worth it, I can't eat all these, and we've got to get them back downstairs."

"Yeah, whose stupid idea was it anyway?"

"Rolo's!"

We all burst out laughing.

Ogden's Club was the highlight of the week. All the girls going out Friday night turned up for work with a head full of rollers, covered by a scarf that was called a turban. We would all be trying to do our work laughing and talking about what pub we were going to meet up in and what time.

"What are you wearing tonight, Bunny?"

"Don't know Joyce, maybe black skirt and a white blouse."

"Oh eh, Bunny, you'll look like the waitress in that cafe we went to last week!"

"Don't!"

"Ya will, the black skirt is okay, but forget the white blouse."

"Oh! What are you like!"

"I liked that pink sweater you had on last week."

"That's our Barbara's, can't wear that again, she'll know."

"Well, what about the blue top, or is that your Barbara's?"

"No, it's mine, but I don't think my Mam's washed it. Anyway, what are you wearing?"

"Don't know. If our Jeanette was still at home I could have taken a chance and pinched her black blouse."

"Oh, come off it Joyce, the size of you to your Jeanette!"

"Ya cheeky bitch!"

"Well, it's true!"

"I know it's bloody true, but you don't have to say it."

"Do ya think we'll get a tail home tonight?"

"Put it this way, Bun, if I don't then I won't be happy."

"Why?"

" 'Cos I'm skint this week, I owe Nan half a crown from last week and I forgot all about it until this mornin, when she reminded me."

"So how much have you got?"

"Well if Nan forgets again, which I doubt, tops ten bob."

"Why worry, there's eight of us going out

tonight, we'll get a kitty up."

"Well, as long as it pays for a taxi into town, I should be okay."

"We could bus it."

"Give over, it's teamed all day and it's blowing a gale. What about my head?"

"Use a brolly if it's still raining."

"Give over Bunny, I've lost a brolly every time we've gone out, and last week it was Nan's. She keeps asking for it. I'll have to go to Greaty market tomorrow and get her one."

"If you run short, I'll fix you up."

"You might have to. If you get a tail home tonight, don't you just go without saying."

"Don't be daft."

"Never mind don't be daft! I'll have to walk home unless I get a tail to pay my bus fare."

"Do you think that Dave fella will be there?"

"What Dave fella?"

"That tall dark haired, blue eyed fab dancer Dave."

"Oh, you did notice him then?"

"Come off it Joyce, he's gorgeous."

"He's okay."

"I wouldn't mind copping off with him."

"In your dreams, Bun!"

"Anyway, you didn't say what you are wearing."

Getting up from my box to go for a sly ciggy, I looked down at Bunny saying, "Now listen, white bra, white drawers, white underskirt, white roll on, black skirt and a white blouse."

"Oh get lost, you've just told me not to wear them."

"Ask a stupid question."

"Are you going to be like this tonight?"

"Like what?"

"Acting daft."

"Tonight, Bunny, I'm going to have a ball on ten bob, two cherry B's and I'll dance the leg off myself."

"Oh, eh girls, have you heard this one?"

"If Mr Walker asks where I am, just say I've gone the lav for a wee, okay?"

"No, I'll tell him you've gone for a ciggy."

"Oh, yeah!"

★ ★ ★ ★ ★

It was always the Dee Vaults in West Derby Road for a quick lager and lime, then into town to the Legs of Man for a few more drinks. We would fall in the Big House on Lime Street to catch a glimpse of a fella dressed as a woman who worked behind the bar. Screaming with laughter, we would all try to get into a taxi back up to Ogdens Club. We would take it in turns to sit on the taxi floor, so the driver didn't lose his licence by taking one too many of us. Some taxi drivers would shout at us to get another taxi, "Now come on girls, I'm only taking six, you two out."

So we all got out. Sod that, one out all out. With a bottle of Ozzy Whites in one of our bags, we headed right for the toilets, trying to pass the bottle round for us all to have a swig while checking our stockings and make-up, before our parade of the club to see where the best looking fellas stood. A few times we fell out over a fella who never fancied any of us anyway. Yes, this was the Swinging Sixties, good clubs, great music and a group of lads called The Beatles who had made their first record. They were local – in fact, from just down the road to us.

My life was in full swing and we sang our hearts out in work to all the up and coming groups. One bottle of Cherry B or a bottle of Pony and we were foot tapping and dancing the night away. The big underskirts were still all the rage, some made of sponge or if you had a few bob, you could buy the lacy ones that would take ages to starch to make them stick out, but would rip the stockings off your legs being so stiff.

We wore elastic belts called wassy belts that we

stitched to make smaller so they pulled your waist in, half of us should have needed hospital treatment by the end of a night out because we couldn't breath, they were so tight. On our feet we wore ballerinas made from soft velvet, they cost us about one and six, but two and six if they had sequins on, but that fashion didn't last long as all the pointed toe shoes started to come out. The points were always two inches longer than your big toe, so everyone looked like they had big feet.

Ties on the fellas went from big wide ones to very thin ones, some looking like boot laces. The Teddy Boys started to look old fashioned as the local lads had been following The Beatles and their hair was more down on the face with no Brylcream, in fact very neat and clean looking.

All the styles had started to change, even to the point of skirts. The skirts had gone very short and it was just as well tights had come into fashion, as it was impossible to wear skirts that short with stockings. The fella's were not too happy about tights being the fashion for girls, it sort of restricted them in more ways than one, but the short skirts made up for it. Now, fella's can't have the best of both worlds can they?

We would also go to Burtons at the bottom of Spellow Lane. That ended up being our regular dance hall, and all the same crowd used to go each week. They never sold beer only soft drinks, so we would go the pub first, then on to the Burtons. All the fella's came in about quarter past ten right out the pub, and would stand at the back of the hall to weigh up the talent.

On one such night, I had my eye on this fella who was the spit of Dean Martin, but never thought in a hundred years he'd ask me to dance. All the girls had sat down for a gab and a ciggy when he walked across the floor to ask one of us up. I nearly died when he stopped by me.

"Gettin up?"

"Yeah, okay."

All the girls where totally gob-smacked, as he kept me up for the rest of the night dance after dance. When it was time to leave, he said, "Get your coat."

Fella's didn't ask those days if could they take you home. You always knew once they said get your coat, you had a tail home, but that was after they found out you lived within a two to three mile area. If they missed their last bus, it wasn't far for them to walk home. We all knew we were on for a tail if the fella asked, "Do you live around here?"

If we didn't like the fella, we always said "No, we live in Kirkby." Most of the time you got away with it. Anyway getting back to this Dean Martin look-alike, we got the bus home back to Salva Street. All the girls where on the same bus as us, and in turn getting off at their stops said, "Good night Joyce, don't do anything I wouldn't do!", or some of my mates just smiled and said, "See you tomorrow."

We stood at the top of Salva Street just by the entry and I was ready to have my first kiss with this gorgeous fella, when I felt a tap on my shoulder, "What the hell are you up to?"

"Oh, Nan, I didn't see you."

"I know you didn't. I've been waiting on the step for you, m'lady. What time do you call this?"

"Oh, eh, Nan, I feel ashamed."

"Never mind, what do you think your up to?"

My Dean Martin look-alike was off like a shot, I never even got time to kiss him.

"Thanks, Nan, thanks very much."

"Never mind, you get yourself in."

I walked down our street, while Nan was still going on and on about waiting for me by the door.

"For God's sake, Nan, I wasn't doing anything wrong."

"No, but you would have done if I hadn't walked up the street."

"You're just bad minded. You know the saying, 'what badness thinks, badness does'. If I wanted to be up to no good, I'd have done it years ago."

"You cheeky little sod! Don't you talk to me like that, and don't you raise your voice at me."

"Why not, all you ever do to me is shout and scream."

"You're just sixteen years of age, I'm not having you talk to me like that."

"Oh, so you remember my age? Funny that, you didn't remember the day I was born did you?"

"What the hell are you goin' on about now?"

"You know damn well what I'm goin on about. It's funny isn't it, you know our Gordon's birthday, oh yes, and you know your little blue eyes' birthday, but mine. Now let me think, just give me a minute, I'm not really sure, is it the tenth or the twelfth, oh, I just can't remember, so let's say it's the twelfth, shall we? Is that what you said, well, was it?"

"Don't be so bloody stupid!"

"Oh, I'm not the one to be stupid, it's you!"

With that Nan slapped me so hard across the face, I could feel the tears raise in my eyes, and my nose started to run. I screamed at Nan and pointed my finger in her face, "Don't you ever dare put your hand on me again. Now I'm warning you, touch me again it will be your last. The only thing I will ever remember you for, is your shouting and the belts I've taken. Well no more, that was the last!"

I ran upstairs thinking I had to get away.

The next day all the girls were asking how I'd got on with Dean Martin, and was I seeing him again.

"Oh, you've no idea girls, he was just lovely."

"The state of you."

"I've got a date on Saturday night with him."

"Oh go away, where are you goin'?"

"Don't know till he comes for me."

"What times your date?"

"He said about seven o'clock."

"Oh, eh Joyce, must be taken you somewhere nice then."

Little did the girls know I didn't even get to kiss him and to top it all, now I had to stay in Saturday night, instead of going out with the girls, God, the way lies back fire on you.

"Okay, all the girls have gone now Joyce, what really happened?"

"What do you think, Bun? Nan caught me at the top of our street, just when we were goin' to have a snog."

"Oh, you're jokin!"

"I wish I was."

"Did you feel ashamed?"

"Of course I bloody did! I won't be goin' to Burtons now for a few weeks."

"Don't be daft."

"Oh come off it Bun, I'll never be able to look at him again. I'm fed up lately, don't know what's to do with me, but I'll tell you this, I'm goin to start looking for a flat. Don't get me wrong, Nan's great, but when she turns, she turns and it's always me that gets it."

"Why?"

"I don't know. We can be great for ages then for no reason she kicks off. She started on our Gordon as well this week. She wants more money off us. Bun, she gets most of my money, and she's got no chance with our Gordon, you know what he's like, dead tight."

"Oh, you're awful saying that about your kid."

"But it's true, oh, let's change the subject, I'm depressed now."

"Well, I don't want to depress you anymore, but I gather you're not out this Saturday?"

"Shut up!"

"I only asked."

"Just shut up!"

Another good place to go in the Sixties was the Locarno on West Derby Road, what I'd call a good place to cop off. All the fellas would stand around the outside of the dance floor to watch the girls dance or twist, as that as well as a good jive was the latest dance out. Most of the fellas didn't ask you to dance, they would give you a nudge with their elbow and look towards the dance floor, that always meant "are you dancing?"

Because of my Dean Martin look-alike I'd started to go back to the Locano dance hall. All the girls had found out the truth in the end, so it was a bit of a joke, most of the girls where still going to Burtons, and would tell me whether he was still going.

I didn't mind the Locarno because it was nearer home, so we could just walk home if we didn't have the bus fare. It never took us long, because of the laughing we did, talking about the ugly fellas that tried to cop off with us. I always got the ugly ones! But that's the way it goes, some weeks I'd get lucky.

One such night in the Locarno, I was to meet my future husband, Peter – not that I fancied him when I was dancing! No way! It was the way he dressed!

He just didn't have the right colours on – he wore a green suit, red shirt and brown shoes. Now this fella was shouting that he didn't have an older brother to show him how to dress properly or a sister that cared what her brother wore and that put me off. If I did have a date with Peter, it would have to be where no one knew me until I could teach him what goes with what etc.

We did go to a pub out of the way, which was unknown to Peter and yes, I did change his dress sense. Now, I'm not going to say that our courtship was a good one, we did nothing but argue! Most of the time it would be over stupid things like, "Who's that fella over there, do you know him?"

"What fella?"

"The fella by the bar, he's been looking at you all night."

"Don't be daft!"

"I've seen you givin' him the eye."

"I don't know what you're talkin' about."

Actually, I did know what he was talking about, I'd had my eye on that bloke all night! Well, let's face it he was gorgeous.

"Come on, drink up, we're goin'!" said Peter, in a huff.

"No, I like it here."

"I don't, come on."

"What the hell's up with you? Just 'cos that fella is looking over, you want to go?"

"Look, if you want to stay, then stay, I'm off."

"Go on, then."

I'd no sooner said it, and Peter was gone. I couldn't believe it, he walked out and left me just sitting there. I felt as if the whole pub was looking at me. I finished my drink and walked out into the road to see if I could see Peter. He only sailed past me in a taxi! Well, the lousy sod! *Right, that's it*, I thought, *he can sod off*.

"You're home early." said Nan, as I walked in.

"We had a row."

"What over?"

"Some fella in the pub was looking over at me and Peter didn't like it."

"I wouldn't have that! If he's like that now, you won't be able to move."

"If he calls round, just say I'm out with the girls, don't say anything else. I don't want him knowing I've told you."

"Do you think he will call?"

"No. Any tea in the pot, Nan?"

"Yes, fancy a piece of toast?"

"Go on then."

Nan walked into the back kitchen, "Someone's at the door, what shall I say if it's Peter?"

"Oh, Nan, say I'm not home and you thought I was out with him. It'll give him something to worry about. Don't let him in!"

"Oh, it's okay Joyce, it's Jeanette."

"Who were you expecting?" asked Jeanette, full of curiosity.

"Our Joyce thought you were Peter, they've had a row."

"I'm sure I've just seen him at the top of our street."

"Your kiddin'!"

"I promise you I'm not."

"What's he doin'? Just standing there?"

"Yeah."

"Oh, he must think I'm still walking home. Nan, if he knocks, don't forget what I told you to say."

"I won't, don't worry."

Over a cup of tea, I told our Jeanette what had gone on and Peter walking out on me.

"Was you givin' the fella the eye, then?"

"No." I lied.

"Give over Joyce, bet you was!"

"Well, he was looking over at me."

"I don't blame Peter then."

"Why? He doesn't own me."

"Yeah, but you have been goin' with him a while and let's face it, he's a good fella, that Peter."

"Oh, you don't know him."

"Look Joyce, if you're not sure about him, then why don't you tell him? It's no good stringing him along, it's not fair."

"You and your Tommy didn't row then?"

"Not over another fella, no."

"Come off it! I don't believe that."

"We didn't!"

"Well, you wouldn't, would you, our Jeanette?"

"Oh, don't start – see, that's you all over, it's never your fault is it?"

"What do you mean don't start, it's got nothing

to do with you. Anyway, what have you come over for."

"I wanted a drop of milk for the mornin'."

"What? Not like you, Miss Super-Efficient, to run out of milk," I said sarcastically.

"Nan, can you spare any milk please? I'm goin' home, she's gettin' on my nerves."

"What? Now?"

"You want to get a grip of yourself and grow up."

"Oh, here we go again!"

"Joyce, just... what's up with you?"

"I've come home 'cos I've had a row with Peter and then you come in and start."

"Thanks Nan, give it you back tomorrow."

Nan handed Jeanette a pint of milk and saw her to the front door, "Goodnight love, see you tomorrow."

"Night Nan."

Shutting the door, Nan looked across to me, "There was no need for that."

"Nan, give it a rest."

"You would never think you two were sisters, the way you fight all the time. How long is this goin' on for?"

"As long as it takes."

"Our Jeanette never says anything wrong about you, but you're always ready to have a go at her, the minute she walks in the door."

"The row with Peter had nothing to do with her."

"Then why tell her then?"

"I didn't think she was going to put her oar in, that's why."

"She was only sayin' the other day she was made up for you now you've met a really nice fella."

"Did she now?"

"Yeah, she did, and you're always ready to jump down her throat."

"Do you know why? I hate her, that's why – Goody Two Shoes."

"Always back to Jeanette."

"Yeah, that's right, you rammed it down my throat for years about me not being like Jeanette and who got pregnant? Not me! No, Jeanette did. You throw it up at me for years that I'd bring shame to the house, well, have I?"

"No, you haven't," admitted Nan.

"Why Nan? Why have you always said these things to me? I've never heard you say a good word about me. All these years, no matter what I did you never once gave me credit. It was always Jeanette who could do it better."

"Now come off it, I didn't."

"Oh, yes, you did!"

Nan followed me into the back kitchen to make a pot of tea, "Leave it Nan, go on in, I'll do it."

"Joyce, I didn't realise."

"You never do, Nan."

"I love you all the same."

"Come off it Nan, you're talking to me now."

Nan didn't realise it was far too late now to turn the clock back, she'd hurt me so much over the years.

"Nan, how many toast do you want?"

She'd gone. Suddenly she was back, saying quietly, "Joyce, Peter's at the door."

"What? At this time? You haven't let him in have you?"

"It's no good talking on the step, he's in the kitchen."

"Oh eh, Nan, why didn't you say I was in bed then?"

"I'm taking my tea and toast up, you go and talk to him, but don't be late. Okay?"

"Okay, night Nan."

I walked into the kitchen with my tea and toast. "You've got a bloody cheek," I said to Peter.

"Look, I'm sorry about tonight."

"Oh, are you now?"

"I went back for you."

"Oh yeah? That's funny, I saw you in the taxi."

"No, you didn't."

"I did! And what were you doin' standing at the top of the street? Think I got a tail home did you, from the fella at the bar?"

"You knew him, didn't you?"

"Don't you raise your voice at me! Keep it down, my Nan's in bed!"

"Did you know him?" Peter repeated.

"Look, go home will you, I've had a lousy night with you, Jeanette and Nan. Now sod off, go home."

"That's it then?"

"Yeah, that's it, I've had enough."

Peter got up to go. He picked up his cigarettes and lighter and stood by the open door, "Is that it then?"

"Yeah, how many times do you want me to say it?"

"See ya, then."

"Yeah."

I slammed the front door behind him, put the lights out and went to bed, *Bloody men*, I grumbled on the way upstairs.

I didn't see Peter for about a week. Then one day as I left work, there he was waiting outside for me.

"What do you want?"

"We need to talk. Fancy going for a drink?"

"Peter, all we do is argue."

"Look, let's just go for a drink tonight. I need to talk to you."

"Okay, see you about eight o'clock."

When I got home, I told Nan. "Nan, Peter was outside work, we're going for a drink, so I could be late."

"That's good, told you he would be back," she said, with a smile.

"Where's my purse? I'm goin' over to Margaret Street for a bath, I stink of tobacco – that's the only thing about Ogdens, you can't get rid of the smell, I'm thinking of changing my job."

"Doing what?"

"I'm not sure, keep the *Echo* for me, I'll have a look when I get back, there might be some jobs in it I fancy."

"All right, there's a clean towel in the cupboard upstairs."

"Thanks, Nan."

"See ya later love."

"Se ya, Nan."

"Oh, Nan! Before I go, do us a favour, would you press that skirt for me?"

"Where is it? What about your top?"

"No, just the skirt, it's on my bed."

"All right, see you later."

"Tara."

"Joyce! Where you off? The baths?"

"Hi Ruby, I'm goin' for a bath not a swim, fancy walking up with me?"

"Can't, I'm off to the pictures tonight."

"Who with?"

"Tommy."

"You still seeing him?"

"Don't be hard-faced, we're gettin' married next year."

"Give over! You're too young."

"What about that Peter fella? You've been with him some months, eh."

"Yeah, twelve."

"You'll be next, you wait and see!"

"Get lost, we're not even engaged yet."

"He's slow, isn't he?"

"Yeah, you could say that. Ruby I've got to go or I'll end up gettin' washed in the sink."

I just made it to the baths. We used to pay nine pence to have a bath there. We had long stopped dragging the old tin bath in out the yard because by the time you waited for the water to boil on the stove, you could have been to the baths and back. Most people who didn't have a bathroom used the one in Margaret Street. There were about eight in all, and you just waited until one was free, then the woman would wash it out after the last person, and using a big key, would turn the water on to fill the bath.

At ten to eight Peter was knocking on the door.

"Hi, come in, I'm nearly ready."

"Hello, Mrs Gill."

"Hello Peter. Goin' anywhere nice?"

"Yeah, into town."

"Don't have her back late, she's got work tomorrow."

"Nan! I'm not worried about work, I've told you, I want to leave Ogdens."

"And what are you supposed to do for money?"

"Get another job."

"Oh, just like that?"

"Oh, Nan, don't start, I'm going to get another job."

"Don't leave me without any wages, I kept you for a week with no money."

"When?"

"Ya worked for two weeks and only give me one lot of money."

"Nan, I worked a week in hand, everyone does that, it's the way it goes."

"That's what you say."

"Nan, I picked up three pound thirteen shillings, and I gave you, or should I say you took the three pound and give me the thirteen shillings. Anyway you spend the wage packet not me."

"I don't care, you're not leaving me with no money."

"If I get another job, they pay me that week when I leave, you can have it then. Christ! I can't do no more."

"Joyce, you try and get board and lodgings for the money you give me, you won't find it."

"Oh, I don't believe this, come on, Peter, let's go."

"What was all that about?" Peter asked when we were outside.

"Peter, just leave it, okay?"

"Right. Where do you fancy going?"

"Well, not to town, it's too late now."

"Okay, we'll go up Breck Road."

"I don't care where we go, anywhere you like."

We found a pub and went in. "What do you want, Joyce?"

"Lager and lime, please."

As Peter went to the bar, all I could think about was the things Nan had said, it was starting to put a damper on the night, until Peter came back from the bar.

"Look," he began, "I know things haven't been too good between us lately, but I really think we can make a go of it."

"What do you mean?"

"Shall we get engaged?"

Peter could have knocked me over with a feather. I hadn't expected him to say that. I thought he just wanted to say sorry for last week, and let's have another go, but not this. Looking back, maybe I said yes for the wrong reason, I don't really know, but that was the answer I gave.

Peter was well pleased, and we finished the night off better than the way it had started. We made all sorts of plans, what we were going to do over the next few weeks, what kind of ring I wanted, marriage, children, the lot. We talked all night long.

It was about eighteen months into my relationship with Peter and I felt that I just couldn't take anymore from Nan, so I decided to get a flat down Townsend Lane.

The only thing Nan missed about me was my wages as by then, I'd started to work in another factory called Jacksons the Tailors in town, and the money was just as good as at Ogdens Tobacco. The overtime was there if you wanted it and as long as I'd give Nan a decent wage, the rest was mine.

Moving out was on my mind for a long time, so I'd worked all the hours God sent to get a few bob behind me to help move out. The few bob I'd put away came in handy sooner than I thought as one hell of a row broke out at home, one good ding-dong row and guess what, our Jeanette was the topic of it.

Although Jeanette was well married by then and ready to have her second son, for years I'd had it thrown in my face about not being like her, now I was hearing that I was going to end up like her, having to get married! Well, you name it, I said it, it was time to leave and try to live my life not the life of my elder sister.

I'd seen a card in a shop window advertising for a flat. Peter and I had walked up the street a few times just to have a look at the home. Nan used to say you can tell a clean house by the curtains.

"Joyce, what do you want to do?"

"What do you think?"

"Well, it's no good walking up and down the street, we might as well knock on the door."

"You knock."

"Come on then, it's worth a look."

Peter knocked on the door. It was opened by a well kept looking lady.

"Good morning, we saw your advert for a flat."

"Oh yes, come in, who's it for?"

"It's for my girlfriend, Joyce."

"Oh, that's okay, I don't want couples you see, the flat's far too small."

"No, it's just for me," I said, smiling at her.

"My name's Mrs Evans, well, Margaret."

"This is Peter, my fella, I'm Joyce."

"Right, Joyce, the rent is two pounds a week."

"That's fine."

"Now, if you want we can come to some arrangement about meals. As you can see, we are still waiting for a small table top cooker, so I was wondering, you could have the same meals as the family."

"That's not bad Joyce," said Peter, "at least you will have a hot meal when you come in from work."

"So what's the difference, then?"

"Let's see, would you want a meal every night? You won't be going to your boyfriends, then?"

"If I do, I'll just leave you a note."

"What about Saturday and Sunday?"

"No, you can leave the weekend out."

"Okay, let's say three pounds ten, how's that?"

"That's okay by me."

"Now, Joyce, I won't like Peter staying over."

"Oh, he won't be, don't worry about that."

"It's not that, I just don't think my fella would be too pleased, we only have one bathroom you see."

"What's one bathroom got to do with it?"

"It's upstairs and my two daughters sleep upstairs."

"Still don't know what you mean."

"Well, let's say if it was your fella that wanted the flat, I would have said no, as we only wanted a female."

"Don't worry," said Peter, "I won't be staying, but it is okay to come over each night isn't it?"

"Oh yes, but we lock the front door at half past eleven, so would you make it that time to leave."

I thought that getting your own place would give me the freedom I wanted, but this Margaret one could end up like my Nan. If it's my flat I should be able to do what I wanted. I didn't think I'd be staying here long. It would do for now, but not for long. I thought a self-contained flat would be better for me.

"Right, I'll leave you two to think about it. Would you both like a cup of tea?"

"Oh, yes, please."

"Do you both take milk and sugar?"

"No sugar for me, Peter takes two, please."

"Take your time, have a good talk and see what you think."

"Thanks."

Margaret left the room for us to have a talk and look around.

"What do you think, love?" I asked Peter.

"Well, it's you that's going to be living here, so it's up to you."

"Put it this way, if I take the flat, it's not for long."

"I know that."

"To be honest with you, she looks the type to be in and out all day."

"Do you think so?"

"Oh yes, she'd be in with meals, putting coal on the fire and making sure you've gone home."

"If you want, we can knock it back, but it is clean and on the bus route to work. The bus stop's only round the corner."

"I know and three pound ten's not bad, all in."

"So what are you doing?"

"I'll take it then, but if she gets on my nerves, I'm off."

"Just give it a go, that's all you can do."

The flat was one room. As you opened the door there was a highly polished sideboard, in the alcove at the side of the coal fire was a small table with a vase with plastic flowers in the top. The other side of the fire was a cupboard which had the electric meter in. The room had a big bay window, in front of it was a square dining table with two chairs and along the wall behind the door was the bed settee. A nice room, but it lacked the personal touch.

The coal fire was lit, but the room still looked cold. The bed settee was never altered as it was big enough to use as both. The only thing that was wrong with the flat was the electric meter. There was only one in the house and that was in my room, therefore the family would be in and out by the minute putting a shilling in the meter.

I put flowers in the room and ornaments around and it was so nice and cosy by the time I finished. A few of my friends had called in to have a nose, they thought it was lovely and couldn't understand why I still wanted to find another flat.

I stayed at the flat for a few months then heard on the grapevine that Nan was not too good, so I moved back home with the understanding that she was to lay off me or I'd go for good and never come back.

17

All the promises in the world didn't last and the rows started up again, but by then, Peter and I had already made a date for our wedding. It would be on 9th July 1966.

The night before our wedding, Nan made it quite clear she wanted money from me, shouting that I had lived there all week so she wanted her money. She didn't even let me off a penny.

Bunny was very shocked when I'd gone up to her house, to tell her me and Peter were getting married, and that after all these years, I'd kept my promise.

"Bunny, I want you to stand for me."

"Oh, I feel ashamed."

"So you should."

"Trust you to remember that promise."

"Yes I did, but I see you didn't, you never kept your promise to me."

Bunny had married John – a sea-farer at the time, a smashing fella. I had gone to Bunny's wedding a year ago, but not as her bridesmaid.

"Oh, Joyce, I feel terrible now, you wait."

"Yeah, don't you make anymore promises to me, you never keep them!"

"Oh, shut up, don't make me feel any worse than I do now."

"Right, I'll settle for a coffee and a ciggy, okay?"

"Okay, and you can tell me all about what you've been up to."

I was made up for Bunny, she had her own house in the Walton area, not far from her sister who only lived round the corner, and her brother was right opposite. Her road should have been called the Bunny Road, with all the family living right by her. Bunny and John had a lovely little girl called Lesley, so she was okay for a baby-sitter. While Bunny was making the coffee, I was looking around her house, even with a baby her house was sparkling. I wondered if I would end up with a nice house, just like this.

"Bunny, don't expect a big wedding, it's going to be very quiet, what with money being so short."

"Where are you going to live?"

"Well, at the moment, Peter's Mum's, until we get a few bob together."

"Yeah, the sooner you get your own place the better."

"Tell you what Bunny, you fell on your feet, this house is lovely."

"Thanks."

"Nothing has gone right for us, we both ended up in Court."

"Why?"

Over coffee I tried to explain to Bunny that the day I wanted to get married was the day before my twenty-first birthday, and when Peter and I went down to Brougham Terrace to book our wedding, we were told that I needed a signature from my Mum and Dad for permission. Well I didn't have a Mum and Dad, and we were told that Nan could not sign. We had to go to Court for them to give us the permission. That was an experience in itself.

Each in turn, we had to go into the box and take the oath. The Judge asked me about where I was working and how much money I had in the Bank, if he had asked to see my Bank book I'd have died, as I'd said something ridiculous like five hundred pounds, when all I had was a shilling, keeping my Bank book open. We didn't have a penny to bless ourselves. Question after question! The Judge said that I could have been born one minute to midnight and gave us his blessing, also saying that this case should never have come to Court, not for one day anyway.

"Joyce, why did you pick the ninth then?"

"Well, I'd met Peter on the ninth, we got engaged on the ninth, so we wanted to get married on the ninth."

"Oh, eh, Joyce, I wouldn't be bothered."

"It was important to us or we would have to wait for the next Saturday the ninth."

"The things you do, anything like that wouldn't bother me."

"Bunny, it's the way I am."

"Who else is goin'?"

"Colin and Fran."

"How are they? I haven't seen them for ages."

"Fine, it'll be them next, they've been together now for ages."

"Well come on, what colour is the outfit, I don't want to clash with you."

"I've bought a nice cream suit and pink hat. I hate hats but I've got to wear one that day, and pink flowers."

"What time is it?"

"Half past nine in the morning, on the ninth of July."

"Half nine! That's early isn't it?"

"It's the only time we could get."

"Christ! I'll have to be up early then, to get ready and take our Lesley round to our kids."

"The breakfast is at Peter's. We'll have to do it after the wedding."

"How come?"

"Peter's Mum and Dad are going away the night before, and I don't want to be there in case I open my mouth, so I think it best to stay out the way. I've got it all to face as soon as we get back."

"Oh, don't worry, who want's to eat at that time anyway?"

"Thanks, Bunny, I need all the help I can get."

"What about your Nan and your Jeanette and Gordon?"

"They're not goin'."

"Why?"

"Nan said she will see me later on, our Jeanette can't get anyone to mind Tommy and Ian, so her and Tommy will try and make it at night, if Tommy's sister comes down to mind the kids, and you know our Gordon, he won't put his hand in his pocket unless its free ale."

"So it's me and John, Colin and Fran and you and Peter?"

"Looks that way, some wedding this is going to

be. Put the kettle on Bun, lets have another coffee."

"Don't worry Joyce, it will be a good day. We'll make sure it is."

"Hope so."

★　★　★　★　★

My wedding day *was* good. Peter's Mum and Dad never liked the idea of me marrying Peter as I was the only Protestant to marry into the family. Anyway, they thought it best to go to Ireland for two weeks to get out of the way.

Talk about getting married on a shoe string, we didn't have a penny between us. So there I was, dressed to kill, standing at the sink washing lettuce and setting the table, while Peter gave the drinks out in another room to our four friends that had been invited. I mean we did get married at half past nine in the morning and who wants to go to a wedding at that time? Well, that's my story and I'm sticking to it. The truth was, we couldn't afford to ask anyone else to go.

We sat down to eat about eleven o'clock. The table looked lovely and each in turn toasted us, but not without saying hope all your troubles will be little ones. They always say that at weddings.

It's funny how things turn out, all day I was

thinking I'd have liked Nan, our Jeanette and Gordon there, I really missed them. Now I know what our Jeanette must have felt. What goes round, comes round. It's true, looking back I must have put a damper on Jeanette's big day.

The only difference was our Jeanette hadn't told me to go to hell when I had asked. No, she was too lady-like for that. I think I've got a lot of growing up to do. Big Tommy was right, he'd said those words to me years ago.

I hope she gets a baby-sitter for tonight. No one can change overnight, but I can try. She must have had her worries, what with a baby on the way and all. At least we haven't got that worry, but it was obvious her first few years were a struggle, as she became pregnant again only four months after having her first, so that gave her no time to get on her feet. Big Tommy working all the hours God gave to bring in a few bob, not that the buses paid good wages without the overtime.

"Joyce, you look deep in thought, are you okay?"

"I'm fine."

"You sure? I don't think you've heard a word what's been said, have you?"

"Oh, leave me alone, I'm allowed to daydream today if I want."

"As long as I'm in your dream."

"Oh, you are, don't worry."

"Right. Come on, let's get changed then go down and see your Nan."

"Okay, what's everyone else doing?"

"Bunny and John are going to check on Lesley, but don't worry, they're coming back tonight."

"Don't let me down you two, get yourself back tonight."

"Stop worrying, we will."

"Colin, where's Fran?"

"She's in the bathroom. Best put the kettle on, you know what she's like, she'll be doing her hair and make-up again."

"She never changes."

"John, do you and Bunny want a coffee before you go?"

"Might as well, then we can all jump a taxi. Colin only lives up the road from us."

"Thanks John, I'll shout Fran and tell her to hurry up."

"Colin, leave her, she'll be down when she's ready."

"My ears are burning!" said Fran, coming down the stairs, "you lot all talking about me again?"

"Fran, Bunny and John are dropping us off in the taxi, we're only waiting for you."

"Oh, sorry."

"Right, you two, don't you do anything we wouldn't do, we'll see you about seven."

"Thanks for being here today, we don't know what we would have done without you."

Peter stood by the front door and waited with them to flag down a taxi. They didn't have to wait long. Taxi's are ten a penny down Belmont Road.

By now, I'd gone from job to job and ended up in the same factory as our Gordon – Barker and Dobson just around the corner from Belmont Road.

Where we were living at Peter's Mum's house, it was really handy to get to work with the factory only just around the corner. Peter's Mum was good and didn't take much money from us, giving us time to save up for a place of our own.

I'd seen a house going for rent in Anfield, which was advertised in the *Liverpool Echo*, so I rang up about it the next day. The office was in town and told me to come down right away. I couldn't believe it, our own home and better still, the house was in the next street from Peter's Mum and Dad and right on top of the factory.

Now what had I done to deserve this? On the bus home with the house keys in my hand, I was trying to think of what house it was. I'd never seen an empty house in Cupid Street. The only house I'd seen was the one that had no windows and the workmen had thrown all their rubbish in though the windows. No, it's not that one. On the end of the key was a little slip of brown paper saying N°38. On the bus it was driving me mad trying to think which end of the street the house was.

I jumped off the bus and ran down Belmont Road. I was to meet Peter at one o'clock.

"Hiya, I've got the keys, come on!"

"Stop panicking, have a coffee then we'll go and have a look."

"Oh, lets go now."

"Look, you have the keys, no one else. Have a coffee first, I'm having one."

"Okay."

"Did you have any trouble getting the key?" Peter asked putting a coffee down in front of me.

"No, that's the thing, it was so weird. I asked for the keys to look at the house, and the clerk just handed them to me, and asked for them back by the end of the day."

"Soon as we've had this cuppa, we'll go round. I've to be back at work by two."

"That's not long."

"I was lucky to get that."

"Leave the coffee then, let's go."

"Don't start getting excited, you might end up not liking the house then you'll be disappointed. Keep an open mind, and remember, it might need a lot of work doing to it."

"Don't you start putting the damper on it before we've even seen it, come on!"

"What number did you say it was?" Peter asked, shutting the door behind him.

"38. What end of the street is 38?"

"You'll soon find out."

We stopped in front of N°38.

"Oh Peter, this can't be it, not this one."

"It is. Look at the number on the door. I told you not to get excited."

"Oh Peter, it's got no windows, and look at all that rubbish." My face dropped when I saw the mess.

"Let's go in," suggested Peter.

"I hope no one see's us. You don't need a key, we could have climbed through the window."

"That's eleven windows that will need to be put back in, beside the floorboards upstairs. There's about five missing."

"Who pays for that? We can't, we're not going to

take it are we? It's a right mess, where do you start?"

"Take the keys back and have a word with the fella down town. See what he says."

"Why can't you come as well?"

"I've told you, I've to be back at work by two."

"That fella will get the back of my tongue when I go."

"Don't lose your rag, it's not worth it."

"Never mind my rag, I've lost a days pay." I fumed.

"I'll put you on the bus, then I've to get back."

The clerk was on the phone when I got back to the office. I held the keys as high as my head then let them go, crashing down on his desk.

"Can I ring you back, something important has come up," the clerk said hastily, putting the phone down.

"What the hell did you give me these for?" I said, picking the keys back up, "you don't actually need keys, the house has no windows! It's the pits! You want to get yourself down there and see what type of house you're trying to sell."

"I'm sorry, it's years since I've been down to that neck of the woods."

"Talking about wood, it's got floorboards missing as well, and the workmen have put all their rubbish in there instead of going to the tip. In fact the house *is* a tip! You have some cheek you have. And I've lost a day's pay an all."

The door leading from another room opened, it must have been me shouting that brought the main man out.

"What's going on? Can I help you?"

I told the man what had gone on. His name was Melvin Corlinder, and he owned the house.

"If you are interested in the house, I'm sure we can come to some arrangement."

"Yeah, they'd have to be good ones! The house is a mess, you'll never sell it the way it is."

"I'm sure we can. Please leave your name and address with my clerk, I'll be in touch."

"He's got my name and address," I said, slamming the door on my way out.

I waited ages for the bus, I'd just missed one and that didn't help.

Peter walked in the door just before half past six, "How did you get on?"

"Well, you can say tara to the house, I danced on the fella."

Over our tea I told Peter all about the afternoon and what was said.

"If we had any chance of the house, we haven't now."

"Don't you start."

"Why don't you just bite your tongue?"

"And why didn't you come with me, instead of leaving it up to me? You're all the same men, all talk and no action."

"No, I'm not, I told you I could only get an hour off work."

"Next time you do it okay? And I'll get just an hour off work. I lost a day's pay."

"And the house," reminded Peter.

"Sod off, I'm going the bingo."

Now you can't always have bad luck, it's got to leave you sometime and that's just what happened the very next week. We came home from work to a letter from the clerk down town, it said if they put the eleven windows back in and fixed the floorboards back, would we reconsider taking the house for rent at two pounds fifteen shillings a week.

Another day off work and back into town, talk about eating humble pie, because the week before I'd called the man fit to burn. The deal was they would do all the repairs and clean all the rubbish, as long as we moved in right away or put curtains up so no one else would try to wreck it again.

I don't remember the bus ride home, I was too busy thinking about all the things we could do to our new house – our new home.

I felt so proud and started to walk past our house

each day to see if the workmen had started their jobs. I'd got talking to the lady next door, who told me the houses only had a small life span and were due to come down in about five years time. That had put a real damper on all our dreams as the house needed so much doing to it to make it livable, with money we didn't have.

A letter came right out of the blue. If we wanted to, we could put up fifty pounds then pay two pounds fifteen shillings a week and the house was ours. In all, the landlord wanted four hundred pounds for the house and that's just what we did. I put my engagement ring back in the shop for the fifty pounds we needed.

The workmen moved in and the work was done well on time, in a week or so we would start to paint and decorate and go through all the boxes of things I'd bought for our bottom drawer. God, when we came to open the boxes we laughed at all the daft things I'd bought, so young and stupid. Ashtrays made of chalk, plastic dishes, you name it, I'd bought it. These days a car boot sale would turn me away, the daft things you do when young and foolish.

We got the house just the way we wanted it, a little palace, a lot of second hand furniture, but good, it was lovely. The only snag was that Peter was used to a bathroom and toilet inside the house, he didn't know what it was like to go down the backyard in the middle of the night to use the loo. Mind you, I never either. We always used a bucket in the bedroom.

On our first night in our new little house, the first thing I did was to get the bucket to take to bed, much to the shock of Peter, but having said that, he was the first to use it. I think the whole of the street heard him, not being used to having a wee in a bucket, he left the bucket on the floor before he took aim. Being a galvanized bucket, that's one thing you don't do, you have to pick up the bucket and aim down the side then no one hears you. He soon got the hang of that.

The funny thing was, as we opened our back bedroom curtains every morning, we would see other neighbours going down the yard to empty their buckets too!

I'd had a lot of problems trying for a baby and finally ended up in hospital for a small operation.

The doctor said to go home and follow some dates he had given us, but me being me, I told Peter all the wrong dates by mistake and when it came to using the right dates, we were both too tired.

However, we persevered and on 7th November 1967, I gave birth to a lovely little girl, whom we called Jayne.

Jayne was so good, she slept throughout her first two years. I never knew I had her. Other mothers thought I'd drugged her, she was a little gem. Then in 1969, I gave birth to Jason. Now if I'd had Jason first, Jayne would not be here. He cried from day one for the next eleven months non-stop. I didn't know what it was to have a nights sleep or an hour in the day to myself. On top of that our marriage had taken a bad turn for the worse and over the years didn't get any better.

Pushes became slaps, slaps became punches and punches became kicks. You name it, I got it and all because of money, not the lack of it, just the opposite. Peter had worked hard as a butcher and ended up with his own shops – at one time we had six. However, with a mixture of the wrong company and greed he was to end up in prison.

Peter's mate Bob, was talking about a wagon of corned-beef that got delivered just down the road. Bob knew the driver, so for the three of them to turn the wagon over would put quite a few pounds in their pockets. The date was set, the driver would drive the wagon to the back of Bob's shop, all three would unload the wagon, then drive the wagon to the outskirts of Liverpool, then report it to the police as being stolen. Everything was going to plan, until the binmen arrived to empty the bins. The wagon was in the way, one word led to another and the binmen only went and rang the police. It must have looked like candid camera, only this was for real.

They all got five years. First Peter was sent to Walton Prison, then after about three months was transferred to Kirkham Prison outside Preston.

Kirkham is an open prison, which was better for Peter as he got a job working out in the gardens and in the greenhouses.

I used to tell Jayne it was her Dad's factory when we went up each month for our visit.

We would leave our house at nine o'clock on Sunday morning, get a bus into town, then catch another one to Preston. At Preston we'd catch another bus to the prison for a two hour visit, then the same getting back. We would arrive home at quarter to seven at night, one long day for the three of us.

I only ever missed one visit all the time Peter was there. He went crackers. I don't think he realised what it was like, trying to carry a young baby, hold on to another, carry bags, nappies, drinks, the lot, and that's without trying to borrow a few bob for the bus fare. On top of all that, I was trying to keep his shops open.

The day after he went to prison, I was up at the crack of dawn to get the kids ready, to go down and pass the shop keys over to the lad who worked with Peter at the time. As I walked up to the shop, a blue car with three men in, was parked outside. They demanded the keys off me, so they could take over, saying that now Peter was away they'd take over. They put the wind of God up me.

Thank God I came back with the answer, I didn't have any keys and that I was only there to tell the lad the shop would be shut all that day, and it was in the hands of Peter's solicitor. Where I got that from I still don't know. Jayne, by this time, had started to cry with fright. These fella's meant business. In the end I told them I would get the police if they didn't go away.

With two young children and staff that had their hands in the till, we lost the lot. As hard as I tried, it was impossible to keep the shops going and it would break my heart to go up to Kirkham Prison with the kids to let Peter know the bad news.

We got to the prison for the two o'clock visit. What we had to do was wait in the waiting room, then a prison guard would collect all the visiting passes from each of the prisoners wives. When there were enough people there he would then walk us across the road into a building where the prisoners would be waiting.

In the room there were about thirty tables, with four chairs around each. In the right hand corner was a small cafe that sold tea, coffee and biscuits and crisps. All the prisoners were allowed to smoke and would give presents to their families that they had made or painted, asking permission from the Governor first, then the prison guards. Children would scream when it was time to leave, they wanted their Daddies. I could see big grown men upset at the thought of not being able to do anything about it.

Peter would point out different people to me, "See him over there? Well, he was a Bank Manager and stole from the Bank."

"Bet he's got a few bob to come out to."

"No doubt, but he told us he didn't."

"Well he's either stupid or a liar."

"He's not going to say, is he?"

"Well, put it this way, a few bob has got to be better than corned-beef to come out to."

"I didn't want the corned-beef."

"You didn't want five years, but you got it."

"How are the shops doing?"

This was it.

"To be honest, I need to talk to you about the shops. You're not going to like it."

I told Peter all about the shops and the way the staff had treated me, never giving me the day's takings or letting me know what was going on. Stock started to go down. In the end I decided to close each one in turn. I could see Peter's face change.

"Look, don't start."

"Those shops were my livelihood!" he yelled.

"You should have thought about that before you

went on the rob."

"Have they all gone?"

"Yeah, the lot, and I'm not being funny, I'm glad to see the back of them. It's alright, you in here, three square meals, what do you think it's like for us, no bloody money, and do you care?"

"Of course I do."

"Don't talk stupid, you've never cared, you say you do, but you don't. Otherwise you wouldn't be in this place, you never have any luck trying to chase a pound all the time, why couldn't you have been happy with what you had?"

"Oh, don't start."

"I'm just as fed up as you, if not worse, so don't tell me not to start."

"And what makes you think I'm having the time of my life in this place?"

"Tell you what Peter, things are going to change when you come home, that's if I let you come home."

"What do you mean?"

"The Probation Officer said it was up to me if I don't want you back, then I don't have to let you back."

"I can come back home if I want to."

"No, Peter you can't, its not that easy, I'm fed up with you betting on the horses and treating me like dirt."

"I've never treated you like dirt."

"You have, anyway that's the way it is, you've got to change or you'll end up just like this again. Next time you lose the lot, me, the kids, the lot, at least I won't be getting the belts."

"Come on, look at us, I only see you one week in four, and we're starting to row already."

"Yeah, what's new? We always row."

"Come on, love, leave it now."

"I'm just fed up to the back teeth with the lot."

"I've lost the shops, I don't want to lose you three as well."

"Then change."

"I promise you, things will be different, promise."

★ ★ ★ ★ ★

He was coming out to nothing, to help him get parole, he had to get a job to come home to, but that was impossible, how could he get a job if he was locked away? All his so-called drinking partners didn't want to know, no more than myself really.

While he was locked away, I didn't get the punches or watch him putting pounds on the horses and in the early days, watch him walk out the door with the television to sell for a bet. Oh yes, I had the good years, but my God, I'd had the bad ones as well.

The Probation Officer at the time thought he was doing good, but must have been new in the job as he had no idea what prison wives and kids go through. The prisoner was well looked after, but not the family. I never knew Peter had owed so much money to people, unpaid bills, the lot.

With no money and Christmas just around the corner, the Probation Officer came round to tell me to stay in as I was having a parcel delivered for Christmas to see me over. What a Godsend! I was made up and waited in all day. Well, the parcel arrived, and all it contained was three oranges, a packet of sage and onion stuffing, a packet of custard and a box of salt – but not a meal to be made. Whoever put the box together needed shooting. I'm not ungrateful, but to me, it was an insult.

All Peter could talk about was how could he get a job so he could get his parole. It was hard enough trying to keep us together on the money the social was giving me, without spending it on bus fares trying to get a job for Peter, but that's what I did. I talked to all the managers of Butcher's shops, asking for a job for my husband who was in prison. When I look back now, I must have looked stupid. Two kids on tail asking for a job, but low and behold I fell on my feet.

20

I called in to see a business man – his name was Dave O'Connor – who had a factory just off Holt Road.

I knew Peter had had dealings with Dave in the past, buying meat from him. I'd only met Dave the once some months before, when Peter took me to give an order for one of the shops. He seemed a smashing fella, no airs or graces about him, always ready for a chat, even though he was a very busy man.

On that occasion he shook Peter's hand and said, "All right, Peter, how's things?"

"Not bad, Dave, how are you? This is the wife, Joyce."

"How do you do love. Okay, what the hell is a

nice girl doing with this fella?" he said with a grin, shaking my hand.

"It's alright, Dave, you can stop the patter, we've already given you the order."

"Come on into the office, fancy a cup?"

"Another time Dave, we've got a lot to do."

"You should slow down, you must be makin' as much as me now, what with all the shops you have?"

"You must be jokin'."

"Give over, them with money always say they've got none."

"Come on, Peter, we might as well have a cuppa, then we can take the order with us."

"Well, if you don't mind, I don't."

"Go on then Dave, we will have one."

"Sorry about the mess love, just move those papers off that chair and sit down."

On Dave's desk were piles of papers, not in any order, just scattered over the top of the desk. On the side of the shelf behind his chair was an old till that looked like it hadn't been used for years, or come out of a dirty shop. Again there were papers in no order, with a calculator just balancing on the end. Cream painted brick walls that had a big nude girl calendar on, still showing last years date, 1968. Dave must have liked the picture. I'd never seen an office so untidy and it stunk of meat and sweat.

Dave's shirt had blood stains all over the sleeve, and his next to last button was missing, showing his big stomach, him being a well-built man, bet the sweat smell came off him.

The door opened and one of his workmen walked in with three cups, which looked like they'd never been washed, the inside was all brown, with two rings on the inside from the last person, or the one before that. I had one sip just to be polite, but left the rest, a typical workman's cup.

As Dave and Peter talked business, I was looking out of the glass partition into the factory, watching the men bone out and cut the meat up. It was just like a slaughter house, red meat and blood everywhere, sharp knives going like the clappers. All the men were wearing white aprons with the name of the firm printed on the pocket.

One of the young lads came into the office saying, "Your order's ready, Peter".

"Oh, ta," Peter said slipping the fella a pound.

"Cheers! It's by the door. There's your order sheet." he said, handing the paper to Dave.

"Right Dave, thanks for the tea, see ya."

"Take care, tara."

We picked up the order and put the boxes in the van.

"He works hard, that Dave."

"Yeah, you can see that."

"He's a nice fella, always help you out."

It was those words that I had remembered, so thought I'd give it a go and rang Dave for an appointment. I was glad he had remembered me when I walked back into his office.

He stood up and said, "Sorry to hear about about Peter, been a naughty boy then?"

"Yeah, you could say that."

"Sit down Joyce, how can I help you?"

I told Dave all about Peter's gambling. The shops, losing each one. The bad company he had kept. The visits to Kirkham Prison, the trying to live on a shoestring and about the week before. We had started to have electric strikes, at different hours throughout the day, and we had no candles, because food came before light, and I needed every penny for Jayne and Jason, it was better to go without light than food.

Jason, unknown to me, had found my purse, and posted all my money out the letter box in the front door. I had only found out by chance, when I came to put the rubbish out and found a pound note on the doorstep, lodged by the front step. I thought my luck was in, until I came to put the pound in my purse and found all my money had gone, the lot.

I knew it must have been Jason as he had started

to post everything he found out the door. Toys if they fitted, pencils, pens, the lot would go through, then he'd cry to get them back. If only I had done the shopping that day, but I wasn't feeling too good and thought it best to leave it until the next day.

We had only half a loaf and about four eggs in the house. I was at my wits end, who could I borrow off to get me over the week? I wanted to scream, but that wouldn't bring the money back. I felt sick to my stomach, not knowing which way to turn, when there was a knock on the door.

"Hi, Joyce."

"Alright, Brenda, come in."

"What's up?"

No sooner had I told Brenda what had happened, than she was out the door saying, "Won't be long."

Fifteen minutes later she was back with potatoes, bread, tea bags, tins of soup, beans and spaghetti. I tried to thank her.

"Joyce, don't worry, that's what friends are for."

"But Brenda, how can I pay you back?"

"Try putting the kettle on."

Poor Dave heard the lot, even about me going to other shops asking for a job for Peter. I needed help and I needed my husband home.

The neighbours had done their share of talking

behind my back, some not giving a damn if I even heard them. One of the first things I wanted to do when Peter came out was move. We needed a complete change. We had moved out of Cupid Street the year before. The house was being demolished for redevelopment, and the best offer they gave us was Cantril Farm, a brand new house with a bathroom.

The first thing I got rid of was the galvanized bucket. We didn't need it anymore. The carpet we took with us looked like a stamp in the middle of the floor, with the living room being so big, and at last we had a garden for the kids to play in.

Peter and myself knew it would take time for us to get it the way we wanted, but before we had time to get our dreams together, Peter was put away. Apart from the fact that I'd tried to do the garden, painting and decorating, the house remained the same. What furniture we had in the last house, was lost in this one. Now we had three bedrooms, but only furniture for two. Trying to put this here and that there to make it look livable got me down.

Our Jeanette had also moved out to Cantril Farm two years earlier, so if either of us needed a babysitter, we could do it for each other. However, it was not to be, as things between us was still not right, and in the past twelve months we hadn't seen much of her or her family.

Jeanette had a little job in a school, big Tommy was now in another job out in Kirkby and Jeanette's boys were heavily into sport and football. Tommy and Jeanette would take the boys each Sunday to play for the school football team, so I didn't get to see them very often.

Nan would call to see us every week, or me and the kids would go down to her flat to see her. Nan's house had also been pulled down and she ended up in Sheil Road, in a block of three. After all those years Nan still hadn't changed, she would still go on about our Jeanette.

"Oh, Joyce, you should see our Jeanette's new carpet, it's not like this one, it goes right up to the walls."

What she meant was it was fitted, or she would say, "Why don't the kids put all their toys away? Tommy has made big toy boxes for the boys."

Nan knew the position I was in, but it never made any difference.

"Nan, I've got no money, you know that."

"But you did have."

"I know we did have, but we didn't live here then."

"Then why didn't you put some away?"

"Nan, I'm not going to have another shouting

match with you again, if you don't like what you see, why don't you go round to our Jeanette's, or go and visit our Gordon?"

Gordon was married with a little daughter, but his wife was well clued up on Nan, and had also stood her ground. Nan never did get on with Gordon's wife, so didn't visit him. Gordon had to go to see Nan on his own.

"If that's the way you feel, I'm off."

Nan picked up her coat and bag and was gone. Right now I don't need this, thinking as I looked out of the window watching Nan walking up the road. Oh, I wished Peter was home.

"So now, Dave, you have to help me please."

"Well you've certainly had a rough ride, to say the least."

"I'm sorry to go on, I think I just needed someone to listen to me."

"Don't worry, I think we can work things out for you. What you're saying is that if Peter had a job, it would go in his favour for parole."

"That's about it Dave, that's what his Probation Officer tells me anyway."

"Okay, give me the Probation Officer's number and I'll give him a ring. Don't worry about anything for now, we'll fix him up. I also need to talk to Peter. Maybe his Probation Officer will get me a prison pass."

"If not Dave, you can have mine. I'm not due to visit Peter until the week after next, so I'll just write and tell him to put your name on it instead of mine."

"No, why should you miss a visit. Peter will want to see you and the kids. Now get yourself home and see to your kids. I'll be in touch."

"Thanks for all your help, Dave."

"Forget it, I haven't done anything yet."

I took Dave's hand and gave him a kiss on the cheek, "Thanks again. Sorry about the ear bashing."

"Don't be daft, glad to help out. I owe Peter a favour anyway, he's not a bad lad."

After a tearful hour long talk, he gave Peter a job and also went to Kirkham Prison to talk to the Governor and have a short visit with Peter, it worked. Peter was on parole within eleven months of his five years sentence.

21

Peter came home full of promises, he would never gamble again and would work hard at our marriage. He'd keep his hands to himself and not hit me again or go out with women behind my back.

Give him credit, Peter never gambled again, that was the one promise he kept. His other promises fell by the wayside and we drifted further apart.

I knew he was seeing someone, but couldn't prove it as he never went over the doorstep of a night without me. He was seeing someone during the day and on his Wednesday afternoon off. It was a woman I knew and used to go to the bingo with and she had been to our house. She was having it off with my husband and coming into my home, what a cheek!

That hurt me more, she was in our home, while I was making coffee she must have been canoodling under my nose. Trying to prove it was difficult. None of my family would believe me, she was so old fashioned it was untrue, no style, winsyette nightie type, but she must have had something besides her six kids.

One night we had come back from the bingo and the three of us were sitting around talking, when Peter made the fatal mistake, he lit two cigarettes up and gave one to her. The look on his face gave the game away. He quickly handed me the other, but it was too late, I had them. I had the proof I wanted.

From that day on I gave Peter a life of hell, still not letting him know I knew who it was. I don't know how I kept it in, but I did. I came home from work on the Friday night to find Peter already home, to be told he was going away for the weekend

"Fine, I'll go to the bingo with Jean. I'll give her a ring."

"Don't bother, it's her I'm going with."

When you're told something you already know, but don't really want to know, it knocks you for six to say the least and I wasn't just going to let her get away with it, no way.

The anger had well and truly set in or was it pain? I don't know how I felt, my marriage had well and truly hit the wall.

It was August Bank Holiday weekend and Peter was off for the holiday to set up a little love nest in a hotel in Morecombe and would be back on the Monday night for work the next day. The one thing he did say before he left was that the ball was in my court, it was up to me. Now, I'm not playing second fiddle to any woman and told him to go.

On the Monday, I was up early, not that I'd slept anyway. The sun was cracking the flags and most of the families around were out in their gardens with their kids or just cutting the grass, and here I was looking into the future, ending up with no money and two kids to feed and clothe. The anger rose from my boots. After a cup of coffee and about three cigarettes, I rang Jean's husband and asked to speak to her, knowing damn well that she wasn't there. Jean's husband told me that she had gone away with her mother for the weekend

"What time will she be back home?"

"Oh about eight o'clock."

"Right, do me a favour John, tell her I rang and I have a surprise for her."

"Oh right, does she know what it is?"

"Oh yes, she'll have a good idea."

With that I put the phone down. I went through the house like a does of salts, grabbing all Peter's clothes, anything at all that belonged to him and I threw them out of the bedroom window. I didn't care what it was, I just threw it out. The back garden looked like a rag and bone yard, most of the neighbours just looked in shock as shirts, socks and trousers floated down from the window. He could take the lot plus himself when he comes home.

I sank back on the bed, tears running down my face. What the hell was I doing, I'd gone from bad to worse. I should have got out of the marriage years ago.

A few years ago when we lived in our little house before they were pulled down and Jayne was only a baby, Peter used to say, "Fancy going to town on Wednesday?"

Then on Wednesday, I'd ask what time did he want to go and he'd ask me what I was talking about, saying that he never said anything about going to town. He'd play tricks just to make me think that I was going mad. This had gone on for months, to the point that I started to believe that I was going mad. Always doubting myself, now did he say that or did I just imagine it. The weight dropped off me with the worry of it.

One day I'd took enough and decided to take an overdose, only to end up at the Police Station with a policeman standing over me. Peter had taken me there and asked the police to put me in a straight jacket and lock me up. I was carrying Jason at the time and I was about four months pregnant. The policeman sat with me for hours, just talking, then he went into the next room to talk to Peter, to listen to his side of things.

"Look love," he said when he came back, handing me a cup of tea, "the only thing I can say to you is for you to get as far away from that man as possible. It's not you, he's off his trolley, just get rid of him. Is there anyone you can go and stay with?"

"Not really, I've got a little girl and I'm pregnant again and I don't fancy going back to my Nan to live, it would be a step back and not forward."

As we walked home, Peter told me the policeman had said for him to keep an eye on me and that I'd be alright, little did Peter know what the policeman had really said.

That ordeal had taken it's toll on me. The very next week, I'd started to lose blood. The doctor had been in to see me and told us that I needed complete bed rest for the week and not to put my foot out of the bed or I'd lose the baby. Jayne was coming up to two years old and as I'd said previously, she was a good baby, which was just as well, as Peter never took any time off work to look after us. Nan would come over or Vera, my friend would come and make me a drink and take care of Jayne for me.

By the end of the following week, the bleeding had stopped and the baby was going to be alright. Peter was coming home to no tea every night, so I was glad to be getting up to get back into my routine. I made a mixed grill, set the table, did it all nice. Jayne was fast asleep in bed, so we could spend some time together and I'd have someone to talk to.

I looked forward to Peter coming home, but it was not to be. I still say to this day, he had a date that night as within ten minutes he started to row with me. The meal got thrown across the room. I'd ended up punched yet again and pushed over the back of the settee. My skirt was ripped from waist to hem. I ran out of the door and along Belmont Road to Sheil Road to where my Nan now lived. Next morning there was a ran-tan-tan on the door about seven o'clock in the morning, it was Peter with Jayne.

"Here look after her, I'm off to work," he said, pushing her into my arms, then he walked off.

Nan had seen his temper for herself for the first time and told me to leave him. With one baby and another on the way, who could I turn to? Nan had no room for us to stay and I never had a penny on me or a change of clothes for Jayne or myself. I had to go back.

The hate had set in and I began to remember what the policeman had said to me about getting away, but it was easier said than done. I knew from this time, we wouldn't last and asked him for a divorce, but each time he would say he was sorry then go out and buy me a ring or bracelet, each thing he gave me cost me the hiding of my life.

Oh, they looked good on me, but no one ever really knew what they had really cost. To me the jewellery meant nothing only a loaf of bread or food to put on the table if times got hard and in the years I spent alone with Jayne and Jason, they did come in handy.

Jayne walked into the bedroom asking, "Mum, the ice cream van is here, can we have a lolly ice?"

As I stood up, the bedroom looked a mess and a T-shirt of Peter's was stuck on the window ledge

"Why not, come on we'll all have one, where's my purse?"

Looking around the house, I thought of all the hard work we had put into our home. It was really nice and by now we both had our own cars, it had taken nine years to get this far. When Peter had come out of prison, I had sold quite a few things to put food in the cupboards for the kids and tried to make ends meet, so we had to start all over again.

I'd got myself a part time job in the Meccano just off Binns Road, working a night shift, so that I could be there in the day for the kids as Peter was back working in the butchers. I made a deal with Peter that if I tried to run the house on my wages, he could put his wages away and we would build up our home again, it was hard, but we did get there.

As the years went on, I changed shifts all the time to suit the kids and their schooling, to end up working days full time. With two good wages coming in, it helped to get us a really nice home, a car each, plus a holiday. The both of us had done really well, only to end like this.

August Bank Holiday Monday had dragged, as I was getting myself into a state on how I was to handle the end of the day with Peter's temper when he saw all his things all over the garden, but this time I was good and ready. I'd nothing to lose, nothing at all and for some reason that had given me inner strength. I didn't want to duck and dive from his punches, I'd go at it like a bull in a china shop, not really knowing who would come off worse.

At about seven thirty, I put my jeans on and a big blue sweater, then told Jayne and Jason not to go out and if their Dad came in before I got back, to tell him that I had gone to Garston. Now I wasn't really sure what Jean's car looked like, so I took the chance and knocked on her door, to be told by one of her six kids that she was not yet home.

I sat back in my car and lit up a cigarette and waited for what seemed ages. Car after car drove past me, but then a car pulled up right behind me. I wasn't sure if it was her as the headlights were shining right in my mirror. After she put her lights off and I was sure it was her, I jumped out of my car and walked back to hers, she was all dressed up. I'd never seen her like this, still old fashioned, but dressed up. Jean got the shock of her life when she realised it was me.

"Open the door, open the friggin' door."

All she'd do was open the window. My hand was in the car like a shot and feeling around for the door catch. I opened the car door and pulled her out by the hair. Now being a lot bigger than me, I didn't think she would have come out so quick, well, not without a struggle anyway. I had totally lost it, I punched her the length of the street, even bringing my knee up time and time again on her face, "You bastard, you bastard."

I knocked on her door and standing on her door step told her husband that his wife had been away for the weekend with my husband. Getting up from the floor with a bright red blood soaked hanky on her face, she said, "I didn't think you would say anything."

"You cheeky bitch, I've not belted you for sleeping with my husband, I've belted you because you still had the cheek to come to our home and sit in front of me, all the time having it off with my husband behind my back. Your not the first and you won't be the last."

As I walked back to my car, I turned and said to John that that was the surprise I had for her. On my way back home, I saw Peter's car heading towards Garston, but just put my foot down to get home. As I walked up the path in the back garden, I could see all Peter's clothes had gone. I thought he must have them in the back of his car and maybe going back to Garston to pick up Jean and drive into the sunset, no such bloody luck. There they were all folded up in a pile on the kitchen floor. The kids had told me that their Dad was going mad and he had gone to Garston to find me.

Right, I was ready. I got the kids off to bed, to get them out of the way before the big fight with him when he came back. I sat down and lit up a cigarette. I was so calm it was untrue and when I had a good look at myself, there was not one spot of her blood on me. Next thing, I heard the car door slam and the back door go.

As he stood in the doorway looking down at me,

he said, "You are lower than a snakes belly."

With a big smirk on my face, I said to him, "Will you still love her tomorrow when you see her face all mangled up?"

"You bitch, you haven't got it in you."

Slamming the door behind him, he went to bed just as the phone rang, it was John. "Hello Joyce, how are you? Are you okay? Is he home?"

"Yes, he's just gone to bed and if you're anything of a man, you will do to him what I've done to her."

"Joyce, she's just gone to hospital in an ambulance," said John.

"Tough! And you can tell her from me that if she tries to do me for GBH, she better look over her shoulder each time she goes out, as I'll be there and I'll do it again and again. I can wait, I've waited a long time for this, I'm not taking any more punches for any woman, in future they'd better look out."

As I sat in the darkness of the living room, I could feel my leg starting to throb, in fact when I started to rub it, I could feel it had gone twice it's size, to the point my jeans wouldn't come off on the right leg, so it was just as well there was no blood on them as it looked like I'd have to wear them for work tomorrow.

Now there was no way I was going upstairs to bed, just in case he did something stupid when I was asleep. At the end of the day I had hurt his lover and I don't think he was going to let me off with that. On the other hand he didn't really know what I'd done and he didn't believe me when I'd said I'd given her a hiding, as he'd always known me to duck and dive from his punches and never try to hit back. Well, we all snap and today I had had enough.

I didn't want to go to sleep that night at the thought of Peter's temper, it could flare up at any time and I wanted to be ready if I heard the door handle go on the living room. He used to say that he was an experienced butcher and I would be dead easy to get rid of just by killing me, boning me out and mix my bones with animal bones, so nobody would know. Peter said he would mince me up, with that horrible look in his eyes, saying "Dead easy!" *Well, not today pal, I'm staying awake,* I thought, *the mincer will have to wait, I'm not ready yet.*

In work the next day, the pain in my leg was driving me mad, so God knows how she must have felt. Tough – it served her right.

I didn't feel sorry for her, if you play with fire then expect to get burnt. Eric, an old friend came over to my machine to say hello and pass the time of day with me, only to end up hearing the story about the night before.

"You want to be careful. Don't worry if you need to talk, I'm always here."

Eric was a really nice man, who stood out in the factory by the way he dressed, so clean and smart, older than me by nineteen years, but we got on great together. A very wise man, who would try and guide me.

One thing led to another and we went out for a drink. We got on great, it was a blessing for me to go out and be treated nice. Eric had been divorced for twenty years and had three grown up children. Eric was back home living with his Mum. He'd been a Navy man in his day and had gone on holiday abroad two and three times a year. We talked for hours and hours, and he took me all over the world in his stories.

Eric was a man who gave me all of his attention, never looking at any other women who walked through the pub door, as my husband had always done. I really liked this man and his company, we got on great together. I didn't see any harm in going out together for a drink as my marriage was over. Although I still wore my wedding ring, it was just a matter of time now before Peter moved out for good. In my mind I wasn't doing anything wrong, we never slept together, we just enjoyed each others company.

One night we had been for a drink and I was back home for eleven thirty, to be met by Peter, who was waiting for me to come home. He was in one of his foul moods and in his hand he had a big carving knife.

"Get the ring off, get the fucking ring off now or I'll cut your fucking finger off."

He was fighting with me to put my finger on the table so it would be easier to get the ring off, easier in one swift blow to take my finger off! I'd never tried so hard to get the ring off and gave it to him. Peter did no more than go out to the kitchen and cut a V shape out of the wedding ring with a pair of pliers, then gave me the ring back plus the big piece of gold he had cut out of it. It seems that he had seen me out with Eric and didn't like it. Talk about what's good for the goose isn't good for the gander.

"You are nothing but a slut, a filthy dirty slut."

"And what does that make you, you've been at it for years?" I spat back.

"Don't think for one minute I'm going to just walk out and leave you all this."

"Take the bloody lot, I don't care any more what you take, just go, get out of my life."

"That's just what you want, me out, so you can move your fancy man in."

"No, you're wrong."

"Oh no, I'm not, bet you where screwing around when I was inside."

"You think what you like, what badness thinks, badness does."

I walked into the kitchen to make a cup of coffee just to get away from his shouting. I thought he would get fed up and go to bed, but no, he followed me out. "How long has it been going on, you screwing around? Well, how long?"

"Peter, I've told you, we're just friends, now leave me alone."

He grabbed the cup and smashed it against the wall. I left the pieces of broken cup on the floor and took another out of the cupboard. *Oh, what's the use*, I thought, and left the cup on the work top and walked back into the living room, lit up a cigarette and sat down. Peter walked back in, carrying just one cup of coffee and sat down. "I'll ask you again, how long has this been going on?"

"Christ! How many times do I have to tell you, Eric is just a good friend."

"Oh, it's Eric, is it?"

"Yes, that's his name, Eric, and do you know what? He's a better man than you."

Peter jumped up from the chair and before I could do anything to stop him, gave me one good back hander right across my face, knocking the cigarette out of my hand. All I saw were stars and the tears the slap brought. I couldn't find the lit cigarette that put a burn in the carpet.

"You stupid bitch, look what you've done."

"What the hell do you care? Or are you taking the carpet with you when you go?"

"I'll take what I bloody well want."

"Yeah, you do that as long as you go, I don't friggin care any more."

Grabbing my hair back, he was banging my head against the settee, "You little slut."

"Go on, go on, is that the way you get your kicks? Oh, is that it, all you're fit for is belting me, you couldn't stand up to a man. Fella's like you only hit women, your a shit you are."

"I'd rather be a shit than a scrubber."

Peter let go of my hair, then sat down again. "Go on, sod off to bed, get out of my sight."

I lay awake for ages. I could hear him picking the broken cup up off the floor, before he finally went to bed himself, slamming the bedroom door behind him. *Peace at last, God, life's got to be better than this, I'll be glad to see the back of him, it's never been this bad before.* Just laying there in bed, I was trying to think of the good times, there must have been some. As hard as I tried, I couldn't think of any. *My God, what have I done with my life? Oh shit! It's not worth thinking about, he's doin' my head in.*

I'd stopped cooking for Peter and tried my best to stay out of his way. I hated being in the house at the same time as him, as we only ended up again having a row. One night he was going out with Jean. He was dressed to the nines and had the cheek to ask me what he looked like, "Well what do you think?" he asked, turning around, "Will I pass?"

"What are you asking me for? Ask her."

"I wanted your opinion."

"Sod off."

"What's to do with you? I'd tell you."

"I'd know what I looked like, I needn't ask you"

I shook my head as he picked up his car keys and walked to the door. *Is he trying it on or what?* I thought, *what's goin on, for a minute he seemed quite pleasant, he's got something up his sleeve.* It didn't last, he came back in a foul temper. Thank God I was in bed. Just before turning over to go asleep, I laughed to myself, *he's all dressed up and got a knock back, serves him right, isn't life a bitch.*

The couple of weeks before he finally left was a living nightmare. I hated coming home and if it wasn't for the kids I would have been gone long ago.

I'll never forget the 12th September 1979 as long as I live. When I came home from work the house had been robbed. The big bar that stood in the corner of the room had gone, the matching coffee table, all the fitted wardrobes, pots, pans, light bulbs, food, bedding. How could this have happened? Then the penny had dropped, Peter had gone and taken a good half, if not more, of our home with him to set up home with Jean. He must have had it planned out, as no way he could do all this on his own and he left the place in a right mess.

All those years I'd worked to build up a nice home, going without a wage from Peter, that lasted eight years, he had more or less left us with what he didn't want. I was glad he had gone, but angry for the way he did it and the way he had no thought for his children.

23

I sat down to talk to Jayne and Jason, trying to explain that things would now be a bit harder for us, but at the end of the day I would do my best.

"There's just the three of us now, so lets make the best of it," I said, hugging them both.

"Won't Dad be coming back, Mum?" Jayne asked.

"No love, but don't worry, you will still see him."

"Mum, why Did Dad take all the things?"

"He needed them for his new home, Jason."

I looked at both Jayne and Jason, they didn't seem bothered about their Dad, maybe they are holding back, I thought, as they just sat reading their books. "Are you two okay?" I asked.

"Yeah, we're fine, why?"

"Listen, if you need to ask me about anything, just ask."

"We don't Mum, it's okay. The good thing is you and Dad won't be fighting any more."

"Do you feel the same way, son?"

"Yeah, I don't want Dad to come back if you are going to fight all the time, and we'll still see him."

"You might find you'll see more of him now he has gone to his new flat, and I bet he takes you out more."

"Do you think so, Mum?"

"Just wait and see. Right, what do you want for tea?"

"I say a chippy tea," said Jayne.

"And what does the man of the house say?"

"Yeah! A chippy tea."

I hoped things worked out for us better than it did nine years ago, when Peter was in prison. At least the kids were older now, and I was working. No more rows, no more slaps, all I could think about was to bring laughter into our home, and make up for all the past months. I knew they had gone through a bad time as well. It wasn't fair on the kids hearing us argue all the time.

After tea, we washed up, put the milk bottles out, locked the doors, then sat in front of the telly with a big bag of sweets I had bought out of the sweet shop next to the chippy, as our first treat. "Right you two, it's your choice, what do you fancy watching?"

"What's on next, Mum?" asked Jayne, emptying all the sweets on her knee to find the ones she wanted.

"Well, we can watch Coronation Street or Coronation Street."

They both laughed, "Thought you said we had a choice!"

"You do, as long as it's..."

They both shouted, "Coronation Street!"

"Then that's settled."

"Do you want a coffee Mum, before it starts?"

"Yes, please," answered Jason.

"Your name's not Mum," Jayne said rubbing Jason's hair, as she walked past his chair, to go into the kitchen, "Jason, you smell lovely!"

"Oh, Mum, tell her!"

"Now, now, you both smell lovely, you should have a bath more often."

Jayne put the cups of coffee down on the table and looked up at me, "We're goin' to be okay, aren't we, Mum?"

I put my arms around the two of them, to give them a cuddle and a kiss, and smiling down said, "Now don't you two worry about a thing, we're going to be just fine, wait and see."

I could feel their arms tighten around me, giving me a cuddle back. I knew it wouldn't be easy, but it had to be better than the way it had been. Yes, I still had the fight in me, and looked on it as another stage in life, we all go through stages, good and bad, it's how you handled them that really counts.

With only one wage coming in and things to be replaced, I knew it would be a big struggle, but was determined to have yet another home. Thank God I was working full time and in a factory that made toys. All kids love toys so I knew my job was safe, or so I thought.

I'd found out where Peter was living and gave him a surprise visit to ask for money for Jayne and Jason. No way was he going to part with any money, but said he would give me a few bob if he got it.

"Got it? Got it? These are your children and you're going to pay."

Peter drove a nice car, had good clothes and always had money on him and this man was going to give me a few bob. *I'll few bob him,* I thought as I left his door, went downstairs and out in the street to his car, and with my car keys, started to play oxo all over his car. Now each time I played oxo I won, so I had to play again and again. I soon got fed up and began to draw flowers as well.

The phone was red hot the next day. No way was

he going to pay me any money for the kids until the car respray was paid for. Well, that got right up my nose, he was taking it out on our kids. Well, back up to his flat again. Bang, bang, bang on the door, "Look, you pay for your kids or I'll tell your boss you've got your finger in the till."

Peter gave me five pounds for each child and kept it at that, even though now he was well and truly on his feet, driving around in a big flashy car and going out to nice fancy restaurants for meals most days of the week. It did get me down when I heard on the grapevine what he was doing, but what goes around comes around. Every dog has its day and I'll just wait.

It was my day that came first, the Meccano shut down in the November and that was me out of a job. Then my car engine blew up on the M57 motorway with no oil in. Well, I can't think of everything. That was the last thing on my mind, engine oil. As we know, everything comes in threes – and Joey the budgie died.

We had him for nine years and he was a big part of our family. The louder the music, the louder he sang and on a nice sunny day, we would hang his cage out in the garden so he would sing to other birds and the neighbours would whistle to him when they were out in their gardens and he would sing back. When he died we all cried, all the neighbours came in to say sorry. We put Joey into a box with cotton wool and closed the lid. I asked the neighbour next door if he would bury Joey for us and I would take the kids out for the day.

"Just put him in the border and would you dig around for me so that me and the kids won't know just where you did put him?"

I always hated gardening and that was one way to get it done. When we came back home, our neighbour had put Joey to rest and dug all the borders for me. That put a smile back on my face. He did the weeding as well.

The Meccano paid us all redundancy money, so I replaced most of the things Peter had left behind. Well, if he didn't want them, then neither did I. I'm not having his cast-offs. I paid for Jayne to go to Germany with the school; gave Jason lots of treats and blew the rest getting our home really nice and once again, it was. I was so proud – especially as I'd done it myself.

With no job, no money only the social, I sold my car and bought a van, the one with a roller shutter on the back. I put cards in all shop windows and started off picking up someone's fridge or a neighbour's three piece suite from her mothers. You name it, I did it to make a few bob on the side. Once

I moved a one parent family's whole house contents to another house. The lady and myself did it, it took three trips, but we did it. I charged her a tenner. Well out of pocket, but she was in the same position as myself, skint. I used that van for months, but the only people that used it were one parent families.

I've never lost so many door handles, or scratched so much furniture. In the back of the van I carried a tin of boot polish and a cloth. If I saw any scratches, I'd give the furniture a quick rub, so it wouldn't be noticed. I'm sure I polished furniture that I hadn't scratched.

One girl wanted me to pick up a cooker from her brother's house, down the Dingle. After giving me the address and settling on a price, I asked her to come with me to give me a hand. I mean, no way could I lift a cooker on my own. I'm strong, but not that bloody strong!

"Here y'are Joyce, pull up here. Our kid said it was in the back, so we've to walk down the entry to get it."

I should have put the price up. The bin men were due and the people had put all the rubbish in the entry for collection.

"Christ! What a day to pick a cooker up, this entry's filthy."

"Sorry about this Joyce, but it's the only day I

can do it. Our kid wants it out the way, he's having a clean out."

"I take it you have told him were coming."

"It doesn't matter, he leaves the back open anyway."

As we pushed the back gate open, I couldn't believe my eyes. There must have been about fifteen cookers there, most you would be ashamed to give to the bin men to take away. I'd have to wash them first. Looking up the back yard, the curtains on the window said it all. They would have fallen to bits in the wash. Inside a dog was jumping up at the window and barking like mad.

"Well, take your pick."

"Our kid said he would put it to one side for me, but I don't know which one it is."

"You better knock to see if anyone's in. The way that dog's barking, someone might call the police. No way am I going down for robbing one of these."

"Don't be stupid, no one would call the police."

"Don't you believe it, the bin men called the police when my ex was robbing a wagon of corned beef!"

"There's no answer."

"Well, take your pick, that one's not bad, it only needs two knobs and you can take them off that one on the back there," I suggested, pointing to a filthy dirty cooker.

"A bottle of bleach and it will be as good as new."

Well, one dirty family this, I thought. *Her brother must be a rag and bone man to have all this rubbish in his back yard.*

"Look, what are you goin' to do? Leave if for another day or what? Whatever, you will still have to give me the petrol money for coming down here."

"Yeah, don't worry, you'll get it."

The yard stunk. I didn't know if it was the rubbish in the entry, the drains or what. All I wanted to do was go. "I'm not being funny, but I've got another job to do after this."

"Okay, okay, I'll take that one. I'll kill our kid for this."

We struggled up the entry carrying the cooker over bin bags that dogs had ripped open, which meant their contents were hanging out, dog dirt, the lot. We got to the van and putting the cooker down, rolled up the back shutter. "Right, if you want to stand in the van and pull the cooker, I'll try and lift it up, okay?"

"Okay."

I leaned the cooker back to get a good grip underneath, "Are you ready? When I say go, lift it with me."

"Hang on a minute, while I try to get a grip, this grill is loose."

The whole bloody cooker was loose, I wish she'd hurry up. *I feel ashamed*, I thought, *if someone walks around the corner now I'll die with embarrassment, and I've to take it out the other end.*

"Right, lift!" I shouted, thinking she had a good grip, but she didn't and the stupid cooker landed on its side, and fell to bits right in front of us.

"That's it, leave it, just leave it!" I shouted.

"What?"

"You heard me, leave it, get in the van, I'm off."

"What about the cooker?"

"Leave it in the street, what do you want me to do, pick it up and put it back in your kid's back yard? No bloody way."

As I drove away, looking in my mirror I could see a pile of broken pieces of cooker in the middle of the street, just as the bin men turned the corner. Talk about good timing.

We drove a couple of streets away with not one word spoken in the van. I think the girl could see I had a cob on. When I stopped at the lights, I looked at her, then the pair of us just burst our laughing. I never did go back to the Dingle for another cooker. The girl never asked, but she did give me a fiver and a packet of cigarettes.

The word must have got around, "Oh, Joyce will do it and she's cheap."

I soon knocked that on the head, sold the van and got another car.

I had applied for a job on the ambulances. I'd seen girls driving them and thought I could do that. You didn't have to wear your own clothes, they provided you with a nice uniform and the pay wasn't bad. *Yes*, I thought, *I'll give it a go, it's only dropping people off at the Hospital, then taking them home. Easy.*

I wanted to get off the social as Peter had sent a letter in saying that I was cohabiting with Eric. I didn't know what the word meant and no, I wasn't. Eric was not living with me. I didn't want to lose Jayne and Jason's respect and even so, the social took my book off me for six weeks and they never gave me that money back, it was just as well that I'd put money to one side from the van jobs. I told the social that they could go to my home, I would stay there while they searched for any man's clothing.

Peter wanted to hurt me yet again, for what reason I don't know. He was well and truly settled with Jean now, and was making another life for himself. At the end of the day he was hurting his own children, he didn't know I'd put money to one side for a rainy day. It would be his kids that would go short not him. I hated him for this. The social had told me who wrote the letter, unusual for them, but they did.

Well, he got his eye wiped, in one way he must have been laughing up his sleeve. *Every dog has its day*, I thought, *one day he will have his. I just hope I get to see it.* The man who interviewed me didn't search my house, but still took my book.

24

I got an interview for the ambulance service on my birthday, that is my real birthday, 10th July.

The interviews were at Quarry Street in Woolton Village. I'd got myself all dressed up to the nines, a nice grey suit, I looked the part. The interview was at nine thirty and as I walked into the old sand stone building, I nearly died. There were about forty people there and there was me thinking I'd be the only one.

We got told to sit in a class room, each chair had a small funny shaped desk that sloped down the side of the chair, the ones I'd seen on the television that the Yanks used in their schools. We all walked in the room and I went for the desk at the far side of the room in the middle. As we sat down, an ambulance officer walked in and took the stage, so he could look down on us all. I thought that this was a funny set up.

I wonder if we're all going to be called out one at a time to sit the interview, I thought, *maybe we'll get a cup of tea whilst we wait, no chance.* The ambulance officer started to introduce himself, "My name is Joe Bloggs,"

I'm only saying that name because by now my nerves had gone to pieces and as soon as he told us his name, I forgot it.

He said, "Now we won't waste your time in keeping you all here for the day, so we are going to have a few tests. As each of you do the test, the papers will be marked up and those of you who fail the test paper, can leave the room and go back to work if you have a job, or go about your day."

The classroom was full of men and there were only three women – including me. I was definitely in the wrong seat. *Christ,* I thought, *I wish I had sat by the door now, that way I would have just sneaked out.* I had to sit there because I couldn't find the courage to walk out and have everyone looking at me.

The first test was dictation, when you had finished all test papers were marked. Three or four men left the room as their names were called out.

The next test was general knowledge. My God, I could hear my name being called out after this one, but no. One woman and five men left the room. By this time I really thought that I'd got it the wrong way round and by some of my answers, I must have it the wrong way. There's no way that I was cleverer than them, maybe he did say that if your name was called you've passed, if not, then what school did they go to?

The last test was maths. *Oh, here goes, I'm definitely done for this time.* Three quarters of the people had gone so it wouldn't be too bad if my name was called now. I slowly turned the paper over. I was a lather of sweat, my heart was in my boots. I wanted this job and I'd got this far and the stupid maths paper was going to stop me. I felt sick, *well, girl give it your best, at least you've tried, at least you can say you gave it your best.*

I could see all these sums and they looked just like the ones I could never get the hang of at school and the ones that had to be added up didn't go down the page but across it. I started on the ones I could first and started to add up. What I did was split the sum up, add a quarter then the next quarter and soon had the total. Now as I was sitting there with no spare paper, I used my left hand. By the time I had finished you couldn't put a pin between the numbers and I forgot were the quarter started or ended and to top it all, the ambulance officer was now sitting on the window ledge.

Looking around the room, he caught me in the corner or his eye. He seemed fascinated by my actions. I could remember looking up at him, then down at my hand and indicated I might have to use my arm. He gave me a wink as if to say don't worry. Too late now, that was the last paper. The next step was the big interview.

We all sat outside the big class room, only about seven counting myself. We didn't speak for a while, then a lady came out of one of the offices, "Bet you could all do with a cup of tea."

Well, that broke the ice for us all, we ended up laughing at some of the answers we had given.

"Oh, I said this..."

"No, that's wrong, it was this..."

And that's the way we spent our next half hour, over a cup of tea. It must have been the Ambulance Services' way of telling us all relax before the interview. They knew we were all keyed up. *Well, if I can get this far, the next stage can't be that bad,* I told myself. Each in turn were called in. I stood up when it was my turn to go in and thought, *My God, I should have washed my hands,* looking down at them still full of ink.

"Hello there, please sit down," the officer said.

Two other officers were sitting down at the side of the main officer's desk. He held out his hand for a handshake, "Sorry about this," I said, holding out my hand.

"You could have used the back of your last paper you know," said the officer who had been sitting on the window ledge.

"You never said we could," I replied, indignantly.

"I didn't think I had to."

Oh, shut up Joyce, I thought

"What are your hobbies, do you have any?"

"Yes, I like fish."

"To eat? Or do you like fishing?"

"No, I've got two goldfish in a bowl."

I could see the other two officers put their heads down, trying not to let me see them laugh.

"Anything else?"

"Yes, I like walking."

"Oh, do you go into Wales, or do you go to the Lake District?"

"Er, no, I like walking round the shops."

By this time, the two officers couldn't help themselves and burst out laughing. I didn't think I was that funny, in fact I was being very serious.

"Well Joyce, looking over your test papers, you

didn't do too bad, can't say the same for your maths, but on the whole you did okay, and you need a sense of humour to work for the Ambulance Service. Thank you, we will let you know."

I stood up, thanked them and left. The first place of call was the toilet. I thought I had ink on my face or something the way they laughed as I shut the door.

That was the worst birthday I could remember. Well, I waited and waited for the post to tell me yes or no. As we all know, authorities are not the best in getting things done like mail on time. Nevertheless, two weeks later it arrived. We all wait for letters like this, but when they come we don't want to open them. As I did, I prayed out loud, "Please God, please god, let me have the job."

Yes! I'd got it, I wanted the family to be so proud of me. I could hear them all, "Our Joyce is an ambulance driver."

Yes, all those years ago I'd said it, I'll show them and I did. The one person I really wanted to show would never know. Nan had died in her sleep in 1974, and most of my pain had left me and I soon realised I was doing this for nobody but myself.

The highlight was to give the social their book back. The lady behind the glass screen said, "What's your wage, you might be able to claim."

"Forget it, I'll manage without," I said proudly.

Easier said than done. I loved that job and wanted to get on, so I had other exams to face over a six week period. You have to take so much in, I found that six weeks so hard, learning about each part of the body, bones, blood vessels, veins, symptoms and what to do for each patient and what to look for, the tell tale signs, the birth of a baby, I could go on. With people you don't make mistakes. In this job you bury your mistakes and if the truth be known, I found it very difficult, but passed all the exams, by the skin of my teeth no doubt. I did it and anyway, my first day back on the station, I walked in as a qualified ambulance driver.

I did quite a lot of day work, and some shifts when a shift man didn't come in if he was sick. Now it wouldn't be fair to say the ambulance man's name, so let's call him Joe Bloggs. He hated working with me, as the first job we would get would always be a DOA (Dead On Arrival), it only happened when I worked with Joe Bloggs, never any other shift man. Well the bell went while I was out checking the Ambulance equipment, in the back of the Ambulance. Joe Bloggs had answered the phone, for our first job, and yes, it was a DOA.

"Told you, it's always the same when I work with you, you're a bloody jinx!" he said, climbing into the cab, "do you want to drive or me?"

"Joe, I don't mind. You, if you want." I moved over to the passenger seat.

When we got to the house, the female, an old lady, had died in her sleep, although we were not allowed to say the patient is dead. We had to take the patient to the hospital casualty, for a doctor to come out to the ambulance to certify her death. The lady had died on her left side, and her right arm was on her pillow, at the side of her face. Rigamortice had set in, so her arm stayed where it was when we came to move the lady. We asked the lady's husband to follow us on, with his daughter. We put the lady on the stretcher, covered her up with the blanket, and started off to the hospital. I stayed in the back with the patient. Next thing I saw her arm starting to move down!

"Christ Joe! Stop the ambulance, she's not dead!"

"Don't be daft, she's well dead."

"Well, if she is, why is she moving?"

Joe pulled up on the road and climbed into the back to see that lady's arm still moving down. "You soft sod, rigamortice leaves the body, then comes back, that's what's happening now."

"Well, move over Joe, I'm coming up front with you, she's put the wind of God up me!"

I had a run of eight patients into Belmont Road Hospital, the day centre. Patients would have a bath, hot meal and a change of clothes. Most of the patients who went there didn't have any family. One man who I had to pick up lived in Huyton.

As I knocked on the door, he answered, "Come in."

He lived in a maisonette. The council had done the whole block up, new doors, kitchen, bathroom, the lot. The man's hall, living room and kitchen were full of dog dirt, it was all over the place and his flat stunk. When I got to Belmont Road Hospital, I reported it to the sister. On my return run later that day, the sister told me the man was staying in hospital until they could find an old person's home for him. The sister had sent a social worker around to his flat to find that his bathroom had never been used and he didn't have a dog!

25

I was still seeing Eric and we set a date to marry – of all the days it was Friday 13th, but I didn't think God would send any more bad luck my way, but he did.

Eric was a good man in every sense of the word, he never hit me or looked at another woman and although he did a lot for me, he just stopped showing me love and when his mother died, never said my name again.

I would lay night after night wanting Eric to love me, but he never did. All the talking in the world didn't help and it took me a long time to realise that when his mother died, any love he had inside him also died with her.

It was a loveless marriage, no matter how I tried

it never made any difference. We ended up like brother and sister for years, not a kiss or a cuddle, but to family and friends we looked the perfect couple. Music was stopped at home and also in the car if Eric was in it. If I laughed he told me to cool it. I was becoming old before my time. I wanted to be loved and I always wanted to laugh.

We did lots of travelling around the world on good holidays, Eric taking me to places he had told me about years before. Locked in this loveless marriage, I felt so sad and lost. When I would see other couples holding each other and punching little kisses and calling them by their names, it really hit me. I hadn't heard Eric say my name in years. When I tried to find out why, he had no answer to give me. The change in Eric when family and friends were visiting was like looking at another man, the man I'd loved those years ago.

We had our ups and downs as all couples do, but when I tried to open my heart he would walk out of the room and if it was at night, he would just walk out of the room and go to bed. For years I'd lay in a bed next to a man who didn't want to know or would talk about how he felt, was it me?

"Eric, what's wrong? Come on, let's talk about it and try to work it out."

The answer was always the same, "There's

nothing wrong, it's okay, don't worry."

And that was always the answer.

In 1982, we moved house to live in Warrington, to a lovely house that was just three years old. The house was corporation and they know how to put a house together, it was great. I loved that house and wanted to buy it. I was in a good job, Eric was working so we could afford it. All the talking fell by the wayside and to top it all Eric didn't hit if off with Jayne and Jason and it was always Jason that got the blunt of his tongue, to the point were Eric eventually told Jason to leave and go to his father's house.

I know all mothers think that their children are good, but Jason was a quiet lad, never answering back, if the truth be known, he was a bit withdrawn. Jason was working Saturdays with his father to learn the butcher trade, so he would have a job when he came to leave school. It was all he ever wanted to do, follow his father's footsteps and most days after school he would travel into Liverpool to his Dad's shop, helping to clean up after the day.

Jason is the image of his Dad, so I often wondered if that was the trouble with Eric. I never found out. Jason could do no right for wrong in Eric's eyes and I ended up piggy in the middle, trying to keep my marriage and my son. I never wanted to go through another divorce, this marriage was for life, but so was my son. In the end, Jason had had enough of Eric and moved out to live with his Dad and new wife Jean.

Now Jayne was no pushover and would stand her ground with Eric. She loved Eric, but like me was never shown it back and before long, I think she also had taken enough as she joined the Royal Air Force and also left home.

I am not sure what was worse, a belt or a loveless marriage. At least after a belt my ex would say sorry and give me a kiss and a cuddle. Eric would go to give me a cuddle, but then back off. I had started to hate myself, it must be me. I'm not dirty, I don't smell, I wear nice clothes, was I fat? I'd started to look at myself as other people saw me, but gave up in the end.

I didn't feel a woman any more and it started to show, my nerves were always on edge. I wanted to shake the life out of Eric and say, "Just give me a cuddle to get me through the day," but no, sitting with the doctor didn't help either and I always felt so bloody stupid after. "Now it's like this doctor, my husband doesn't love me or want to make love any more..."

Now I ask you, it was the truth, but how do you say it without sounding stupid? The friends I did tell told me to get out of the marriage, but I wanted this marriage to work, although I knew deep down it was gone, but I still stayed.

Being an ambulance driver didn't help, seeing so many people in pain and hearing all their bad stories. I thought it was time to move on, pain at work and pain at home, no, something had to go.

I used to pick up a patient who had been in a bad road accident and take her to the hospital each day. She was a traffic warden and started to tell me all about the job, the good sides and the bad. Now like all drivers, I hated traffic wardens. I found out all her hours were less than mine and she was on fifty pounds more than me at the time.

After a great deal of thought, I decided to give it a go and got the job.

The Ambulance Service were on strike at the time, we wanted better conditions and more money. We used to stand on picket duty in full uniform outside the hospitals. The only ambulances being used were for emergency only. We all felt that we couldn't pull all the vehicles off the road. The police had sent a letter to go for a medical, down at Canning Place, Police Headquarters. I was escorted up in the lift to the medical room, to meet the doctor. We just sat there talking about the Ambulance Service, the strike, and why we wanted better conditions.

The medical was a joke, I didn't have to strip off or anything like that. The doctor just asked me some questions, did an eye test and that was it. Within an hour and a half, I was back on picket duty, never saying a word to anyone. I knew the skits I'd get so kept my mouth shut.

A week or so later, I was asked back for an interview. The police interview was more or less the same as the Ambulance Service, minus the laughing. Three police officers sat behind a big desk and asked me why I wanted to leave the Service to be a Traffic Warden.

"Are you aware you have to take some bad stick?"

"Well, I can't see it being as bad as the Ambulance Service. I've been kicked, punched and spat at."

The police never realised all this goes on and that's without having doors slammed in your face. I ended up giving the police some incidents the men and women have to put up with, from patients and family.

"My God, then you should fit in as a Traffic Warden then."

"I would think so, yes."

The Police Station was just as handy as the Ambulance Station for me, so I was made up. Mind you. I didn't hear the last of it for months from all the family and friends – as you can imagine.

I left the Ambulance Service on the 14th January 1990 and started as a Traffic Warden on the 15th, the following day.

It took some getting used to, wearing the stupid hat, but I fell into the job quite well. When an Ambulance drove past me they would give me the 'Hitler' salute.

The job turned out better than I thought. I really liked it and made some good friends in the CID and other Traffic Wardens from Walton Lane Police Station. We would often go out on an all girls' night out and take it in turns to do the driving that night, so the other girls could have a drink, not that any of us really needed alcohol, as we did nothing but laugh all night, mostly about the drivers we had met during the day, and the names we had been called, and the look on the drivers faces when we would say, "Now, do you spell that with a K or a C?" or, "Would that be a capital F?" when we were told to f*** off. We always asked with a straight face, never a smirk, as that would send any driver over the top.

We all had our stories, good and bad, but always found time to laugh about our day at work, or what we had been up to since we last met.

My phone would be red hot at the weekends,

"Joyce, we're all going the bar, if you're not seeing Mike, do you fancy going?"

Rocky would always arrange who was going out, and what time everyone was to meet and who was picking who up. Rocky's real name was Sue, but I called her Rocky as she has three rottweiler dogs, the love of her life, and treated them like her babies.

Over one such phone call, Rocky had asked me to go to a quiz night at Walton Lane bar. All the gang would be there to make up a team. "Now don't worry," she said, "I'll be over to pick you up and one of the bobbies will be dropping you off, so you can have a good drink, it's the day after your birthday and all the gang want to get you a drink."

"Has Mike got anything planned for your birthday".

"Oh, yes, we're going out for a nice meal, so I'm really looking forward to that. Then we are off into Warrington for a drink. Jason said to give him a ring and he will be over to pick us up, and when ready to come home, just give him another ring."

"That's good of him, Joyce."

"Well, it was his way of trying to make it special for me."

I had met Mike two years earlier, in what the Traffic Wardens call a tea speck. A tea speck is somewhere we can go for a drink and a cigarette, like the back of a shop, out the way from the public eye, in my case my tea speck was to go to Mike's office. He was co-owner of a security firm. Over the past two years I'd started to really like Mike, we got on so well, and always laughed a lot. No matter how I felt, he always made me feel good, and often left his office, forgetting what was on my mind, with the laughter.

I had not seen Mike for a few months as I'd had a fall in work and had to give my job up. In a way it had worked out fine, as I could spend more time with Eric, who had retired a few years ago. Little did I know our time together would only last five months. All the hours we had talked about what we would now do, the places we could visit was to be in vain, I was left a widow, as sadly, Eric had a stroke in the November of 1994.

The next few months were the worst, the house was so empty, cold, the loneliness I felt when the phone finally stopped, and the people stopped calling. That's when you really find out who your true friends are, the ones who are always there for you, no matter what, like my Traffic Warden friends and two CID friends that have always been there for me, both of whom work at Huyton Police Station and always find time to ring me each week, or visit me, just to see how I am.

Each one in turn has asked me to go out, but it's never the same. I always felt lost and didn't like the idea of coming home to an empty house, late at night. One of the Traffic Wardens was getting married the following year and wouldn't take no for an answer about me going. I was told I had to go, it would do me the world of good, just to get out.

Rocky was on the phone all the time, "For god's sake, you need to start getting on with your life, it will do you good and me and Eddie will be there, so you won't be on your own."

I tried all kinds to talk my way out of the wedding, only to fall on deaf ears. *Well, you can't sit here all day,* I started to tell myself, *get yourself washed and dressed, and get up the shops. Now what do I need, coffee, milk, oh and cat food. Don't know what the hell to have for my tea.*

I thought I might call in and see Vera on the way back. Vera was an old neighbour I'd met thirty years ago. We still kept in touch, in all that time we had never had a cross word. Vera was known to call me a stuck-up bitch, before she got to know me. What the hell did I have to be stuck up about? She said that I always walked with my nose up in the air.

"Christ! I forgot to put the hot water on, oh never mind, I'll just have a good wash instead of a bath."

It had taken me longer than usual to do my shopping as I'd called in to see Mike for a nice cuppa and a chat to catch up on any news and it would do me the world of good to have a laugh again, over a coffee and a cigarette. I'd told Mike about the past months, and the nights out I didn't want to go on, even the wedding I'd dreaded.

"Joyce, if you want to go to the wedding, I'll go with you. When is it?"

"What? Do you fancy going?"

"Why not? It's a night out, we might enjoy it."

I don't remember much about the rest of the day. I was on cloud nine, as I've said I really liked Mike. How things and life change. Here I was looking forward to a wedding and a new outfit when last week I would have given my right arm not to go. Now that could be put down to fate.

I don't remember much about the wedding as we just talked and talked to each other all night, neither of us having eyes for anyone else.

The little flame in my heart had started to burn bright for Mike. We really hit if off together.

★ ★ ★ ★ ★

I looked forward to my fiftieth birthday. Yes, it was going to be a good day. Jayne, Terry, Wayne and little Lois had been over the day and put balloons and streamers all over the garden, with long banners saying 'Happy 50th Birthday', along the window ledges.

"Christ! Jayne, all the neighbours will know how old I am!"

"Mum, stop worrying, you're only fifty once."

The garden looked great and my two little grandchildren had the time of their lives, blowing up the balloons and telling their Dad where they thought they should go.

Terry wanted to fill some with water, just to throw at me – no chance!

After they had had their tea and took one more look around the garden, they left to go home. I stood on the drive and looked at all their hard work, so thoughtful. Red, blue, yellow, green balloons all moving in the breeze, some on trees, the fence, the windows. I just wanted to cry. I knew deep down this birthday would be so special, as I'd never felt this happy in years.

The Whitney Houston CD was still playing as I walked back inside. The laughter and noise from my family had gone. Looking around the room at some of the cards that had come the day before, I poured out a large scotch and raising my glass said, "To life."

I couldn't remember going to bed, as I'd done some drinking.

I woke up the next day to banging. *Christ, where the hell is that coming from,* I thought, *what time is it?* I tried to look at the clock. Bang bang again.

I hurried to answer the front door.

"Come on, get up, I can't stay, I've got to go to work, open the door."

"Okay! Okay!"

"The garden looks nice, did you have a party?"

"Yes, last night on my own."

"I can see that by your eyes!"

"Happy birthday, sorry, happy fiftieth birthday. I've been ringing the door bell for ages, and banging on the door. Hope you like your present and card, see you tonight." Mike leaned over to give me a kiss, then he was gone.

What a day, friends came over with flowers and cards and the postman brought lots more.

"Happy birthday, Nana", Wayne and Lois shouted as they walked in the door. "This is for you Nan," they shouted, handing me a present which they had bought with their own pocket money.

Jayne and Terry gave me a hug and kiss, "Happy birthday Mum, had a nice day?"

"Oh Jayne, it's been great, Mike was here at half past seven this morning. Look what he gave me," handing Jayne gold earrings and a CD.

"Oh, Mum, they are beautiful, you will have to keep them for a special occasion."

"Yes, I'll wear them tonight, we're going for a meal."

"Mum, sit down and open the kids' present and here's one off me and Terry. I'll put the kettle on."

"Wow! Another CD. Thank you, Wayne, thanks Lois, let's put it on, I love the 60's music."

"Oh, Jayne, the blouse is lovely, thank you all for the nice presents."

The meal Mike and I went for that night put the final finish on the day. It was so romantic and I didn't have to drive. Jason had come down as promised to drive us to the restaurant. "Enjoy your meal Mum, and have a good time. Mike, when you're ready to go home just ring me."

Giving me a kiss Jason whispered in my ear, "You look lovely, Mum."

The day ended as it had started, brilliant.

Back home I poured a drink out for the both of us, "There you go love, to us. Thanks for everything. The past months, for being here for me when I needed it, and for today."

"Joyce, don't you start getting soppy, you don't have to thank me for anything, I wanted to be here."

"Ta, love."

"As long as you've enjoyed yourself that's all I care about."

"It's been the best birthday I've every had, the best."

"Good."

Working for the Police gave me a chance to have a direct line to the Coroners Office, as for some time I wanted to find out about my family, my father whom I never knew and my Mum whom I knew for only a short time. I'd sort of made it a hobby, our Jeanette said she would also try to help.

We ended up with photographs of the ship Dad once sailed on, his signature, a photocopy of his signing on for a ship, the places he visited, the placed he jumped ship, but the past couple of years we had come to another dead end. It was my greatest wish just to find about him and his life.

My Dad could have got married again in Australia, never knowing that his first wife had died. He also could have a grown up family. For all we know, Jeanette, Gordon and myself could have step brothers and sisters. If that's the case, I don't want to hurt his family in any way, or bring trouble to his door. All we would ask is for a photograph of our Dad. The man we never got to know or saw.

My mind often wonders back to that phone call I made to Australia some five years ago. The lady more of less put the phone down on me. I wonder if she was my Dad's second wife and became frightened. Would we ever get to find out?

Jeanette and I had asked Gordon to help in our search, but like most men, he left it up to us.

Talking about our Jeanette, we made up our differences some years ago, and are now the best of friends. So many wasted years gone. It was at that time when we started to talk about our childhood and both decided to look for our Dad.

We still come to dead ends, and no one has heard of him since 17th November 1965, but we are not going to give up until we find out one way or another. He would be so proud of his family now, his three little children all grown up with lives of their own.

Jeanette has two grown up sons and four grandchildren.

Gordon has two daughters and a son and two grandchildren.

Myself, I've two children of course, Jayne and Jason. Jayne has two children and Jason's partner is going to have a baby in the spring.

I read the contents of the envelope and it helped me understand my Mum's life before she died. The pain, the worry of trying to bring up three young children must have been all too much for her. Little did I know until now, my Mum gave me all her strength and I'd been using it all my life without really knowing a part of her was always with me.

The search will go on and so will my life, it's taken this book to realise that I was also carrying pain and I needed to face it. For the first time, I feel peace of mind. The big school gate never shuts. Your life is just like school, you learn something each day and if you don't then your life has been wasted. Live your life to the full.

In my search for my Dad, I have found someone else I wasn't even looking for.

I have found myself.

The tears run down my face with laughter now, not sorrow. My home is full of music when Mike comes over, not always my choice, but if you love Mike, you learn to love his music - Jimmi Hendrix! I feel as though I'd waited all my life for him, we get on so well and both families are pleased for us. It's a funny old world, I've had to reach the age of fifty before my life could start. For the first time I'm living it to the full. No more tears, no pain, just lots of love and kind words from a man I really love.

Other books to look out for by
Pharaoh Press

Saxon Falcon
Braveheart
Kiss of the Lion

Memoirs of a Liverpool Stripper
A Blue Coat Boy
Pier Head Jump
Haunted Liverpool

Journey of Awareness
A Celebration in Verse

Pharaoh
Press